Punched Cards

Data Processing for
Profit Improvement

Donald A. C. McGill

Associate Editor, *Industrial Distribution*

McGRAW-HILL BOOK COMPANY, INC.

New York   Toronto   London   1962

PUNCHED CARDS

II

44993

THE MAPLE PRESS COMPANY, YORK, PA.

Preface

This book is intended to assist the management reader in his approach to and planning of a punched-card installation. It explains the main working principles of punched-card equipment, how this equipment processes routine business data, how objectives are established, the main steps in preinstallation planning, and the education of both management and employees to the benefits and operation of a system.

In the Case Book some actual punched-card installations are described. The cases have been chosen to show not only routine applications of punched cards but also some of the more advanced applications, such as production and quality control. The second half of the Case Book describes the use of computers and punched cards. None of the systems discussed should be regarded as peculiar to one type of business; rather, each should be studied as an example of punched cards' adaptability to a multitude of data processing requirements.

I wish to acknowledge the generous help and advice given me by many authorities in writing this book. Particularly do I want to thank William G. Karro, International Business Machines Corporation, who read and criticized most of the manuscript and furnished technical information. Various members of IBM's information department—particularly David Love and John Barton—were helpful in obtaining case studies for the Case Book. I am most grateful to IBM for making it possible for me to attend its customer executive course at Endicott, N.Y.

I thank also Warren C. Rockwell and Alex C. Tassos, both formerly of Remington Rand Univac's public relations staff, for obtaining case material and other information and illustrations.

Donald A. C. McGill

Part II

INTRODUCTION

The Office: Profit-maker

It would be unfair to business in general (and to business machine manufacturers in particular) to say that management has only recently become aware of the office. Yet this impression surely arises in the wake of many current encomiums on office "automation." The more one hears about "integrated" or "electronic" or "automatic" data processing, the stronger must be the conviction that management is bound tight by roll-top ideas and golden oak attitudes. The fact is, of course, that, ever since the first typewriter began clicking under the gaslights, progress toward faster, less costly ways of recording, classifying, calculating, and summarizing business data has been marked and continuous. And the further fact that a major industry has been created out of this progress is evidence enough of management's persistent search for office efficiency.

But this considerable progress was quite unequal to the swift changes that followed World War II. No businessman needs to be reminded of what happened. Office salaries and wages, for example, rose more than 60 per cent between 1946 and 1956. The burst of postwar business growth and the legacy of war-born government regulations multiplied the clerical load of the average business. This fact is vividly reflected in the rapidly increasing number of clerical workers in proportion to the whole working population. In 1940, according to the Bureau of Labor Statistics, one out of every ten workers in the United States was employed in the office. Ten years later, the ratio was one in eight; in 1958, it had narrowed to one in seven. The swelling demand for office workers not only drove up wages further but also depleted the ranks of reliable, experienced workers. Top management soon grasped the fact that proliferating paperwork had become one of its prime problems.

Prof. C. Northcote Parkinson, originator of several basic "laws" resulting from his studies of pyramidal tendencies in both business and government, has reported how Marks & Spencer Ltd., a large British retail chain, took direct action:

> Merely by deciding that the head office should trust the branch managers, and that the branch managers should trust the girls behind the counters, Marks & Spencer found that it could do away with time cards, catalogue cards, complaint reports and stockroom forms, thus eliminating 22,000,000 pieces of paper weighing 105 tons. All that they lost was a mass of statistical data of which no use, in fact, had ever been made.[1]

But most companies were unwilling or unable to beat such a happy retreat. Because they badly needed *useful* statistics for profitable operation, they attempted to satisfy paperwork's voracious appetite for competent workers by spreading out the available skills in the office and simplifying individual tasks. This expedient enabled even indifferent employees to serve some useful purpose. But, being an expedient, it proved to be short-lived. In the office equipped with conventional machines, it was found that too many people were needed to maintain even passable standards of speed and accuracy. Quite obviously, the office had become too expensive—and of diminishing usefulness. First in the larger firms, and later in the smaller, management decided that the only solution to office efficiency must be the same as that adopted decades earlier to improve production standards: mechanization.

Punched Cards Revived

The need for mechanization was anticipated by business machine manufacturers who had, especially during World War II, been perfecting an old statistical tool for handling routine paperwork: punched cards. Originated in France before the French Revolution as a means of operating a loom, then borrowed by an English mathematician fifty years later for an "analytic engine," punched cards were first seriously used in data processing by the U.S. Census Bureau in 1890.

[1] "Hard Look at Efficiency Experts," *New York Times Magazine,* Apr. 3, 1960.

By 1928, International Business Machines Corporation had developed the present 80-column card, which through the next twenty years was to become more and more familiar in statistical and clerical operations. During the same period, the precursors of today's wide range of data processing machines were developed—units which could reproduce alphabetical and numerical data punched in cards in printed form.

Punched cards were never generally used for routine processing of paperwork prior to World War II, and even during the war their use was greatest among large defense industries and the government. It took the spurt of postwar growth and the pressure of costs and competition to bring them into general use by business. Since 1947, expenditures for new data processing machines and electronic equipment have increased from millions to billions of dollars.

Part of this huge increase is due to the fact that more and more smaller firms are installing punched-card equipment. According to one major manufacturer, the average punched-card installation now being made carries a monthly rental of $600, evidence that office automation is no longer the exclusive preserve of the business giants. In the space of a decade, the data processing "revolution" has begun to affect all business.

The "New" Office

But mechanization, as exemplified by punched-card systems, has created a "new" office, an office governed by a new set of rules and ideas. It is of this office that management is just becoming aware, for it confronts management with clerical procedures unknown in the conventional office.

With the conventional office, for example, management could improve efficiency by installing new equipment, but always within the framework of the traditional organization. A bookkeeping machine could supplant manual methods and yet leave surrounding routine much as it was. Or a photocopy machine could be acquired to prepare working copies of orders without radically changing the established order-invoice procedure. Despite the introduction of new machines or methods, the conventional office retained its traditional appearance and organization.

With punched-card systems, however, has come a wholly new idea in office management and organization. Briefly, it is the idea of putting necessary business data in a form in which they can be *automatically* perpetuated through all subsequent processing. Punched-card data processing closes the gaps existing between the various processing steps in the conventional office. It replaces the fallible human links between typewriters and calculating machines and bookkeeping machines. With punched cards, the processing of business data becomes continuous, unbroken, and automatic.

Because punched cards have so markedly changed clerical methods, they have also changed the *function* of the office. Traditionally, the office has been regarded as a burdensome but necessary service department of the business, contributing little beyond cost. Its ability to contribute to profits or to influence profits was always limited. The conventional office could analyze and summarize transactions only at great cost and was, therefore, of modest help to management as a profit-making tool. Through its use of punched cards, the new office can, in contrast, provide management with valuable decision-making facts as part of its ability to process routine paperwork. The new office is indispensable to management in the control and planning of the business. Thus, punched cards have pushed the influence of the office beyond its own four walls into every department and into every management level.

Punched Cards and Management

Because of the profound changes it brings about in the methods and functions of the office, punched-card data processing demands the earnest, unflagging attention of management. The success of a punched-card installation is directly proportional to the interest that management is prepared to take in its planning and operation. Moreover, this interest should not be bounded by a superficial desire to discharge office employees and thereby cut clerical costs. Management should, instead, center its main interest on a punched-card installation's capacity for providing information needed to improve the company's profit performance. If this capacity is to be fully realized, management must be ready to involve itself in the many details of setting objectives for, and planning and managing, an installation. A punched-card system is much more than a set of new office machines. It represents a new method of management. No major phase of its planning or operation can be left entirely to subordinates.

1

Punched Cards and Profits

Bob Cratchit is certainly among the best known of the data processors. Warming himself by the guttering candle on his high desk and scratching out Scrooge's ledgers, he meticulously carried out a function as old as business itself: keeping records. The machines that have long since displaced poor Bob's precise penmanship with a frightening ability to print hundreds of lines per minute have spawned a whole dictionary of new terms to displace the old. *Data processing* is, for the moment, the electronic equivalent of *record keeping, bookkeeping, accounting, paperwork,* or any other term describing what Bob endeavored to do to the best of his numbed fingers' ability. Possibly the space age will find another term for data processing, but it is improbable that it will find a substitute for business' need for accurate, prompt, timely records and reports. So Bob Cratchit's ghost hovers over the office still, the shade of the painstaking clerk recording business data in a form that can be understood, communicated, and acted upon.

Whether he was aware of it or not, Cratchit was providing Scrooge with decision-making information, facts which the old man could use in running the business. To this extent, Scrooge's miserable office was making its contribution to his profits. The same is true today, except that management now needs many more facts to guide its decision

5

making. The challenge of today's rising costs and intensifying competition is so general to all kinds of business that management cannot risk a wrong decision. The need for prompt, timely analyses of business data is becoming not only obvious but imperative. There is no longer any question of a relationship existing between these analyses and a company's profit; the question is only one of how much a data processing system can help management make decisions that will improve profit performance.

Punched-card data processing is able to yield analyses of business data much more quickly and easily than manual clerical methods. It can make available facts which have a current management purpose. But the successful application of punched-card data processing depends on management being clear as to its purpose. Management must, therefore, set up particular objectives to govern its control and planning of the company's operations and specify the kinds of information it needs to help it achieve these objectives. Thus, the objectives that management chooses will determine the kinds of data processing tasks that will be assigned to the punched-card system. Unhappy experience has shown that it is quite possible to have a system that fails to provide the needed information because management has not defined its objectives.

Since the primary purpose of a company is to make a profit on the sales of its goods or services, the right objectives can legitimately be directed to this purpose. Consequently, the objectives involving sales, production, advertising, inventory control, and other of the firm's operations would be chosen for their relevance to over-all profit. It follows that there must be some determination of the contribution which the various departments and functions make to over-all profit. And here arises a conflict in deciding on objectives. Each department might believe, for example, that it can make the greatest contribution to profit by cutting costs and raising output. But this approach ignores the possibility that an attempt by one department to improve its performance might tend to injure the performance of another department, so that the final contribution to profit is less than it could have been.

Management can resolve such conflicts or avoid the chance of conflict occurring by (1) taking a *management* view of costs, and (2) setting up profit objectives. The management view of costs, as contrasted with the strict accounting view, recognizes them as potentially productive of profit. In this view, spasmodic or arbitrary cost cutting can work to the detriment of profit because it may ignore the investment character of certain costs. The adoption of the management view of costs helps resolve intracompany conflicts and paves the way to establishing profit objectives for the guidance of management's control and planning efforts.

Management View of Costs

The profits of a company are the residual left after gross costs have been deducted from gross receipts. Notwithstanding its fundamental truth, this definition of profits can create the impression that, where costs are low in relation to sales revenue, a large residual will automatically result. Yet, acting under this impression, the management of many a company has suffered misery where it had anticipated happiness. Seeking to improve profits, it embarked on a program of cutting costs and promoting sales. When the program failed to increase the residual as expected, management blamed uncontrollable costs and an adverse market. In the same period, however, the managements of other companies were able to show a satisfactory profit performance. What were these managements able to do that cost cutting and sales effort were unable to do?

Part of the answer is to be found in the method by which the latter managements *measure* profit. They measure profit in such a way that they know how efficiently the assets of the business are being used. They use a measure which shows return on investment—investment being not only stockholders' equity but also certain costs or expenditures which management deems necessary for profit-making purposes. In contrast, many other managements depend unduly on the ratio of profits to sales as a measure, with the result that control of costs is continually jeopardized. When the ratio falls, management reacts by slashing costs wherever possible and by trying to drive up receipts in the hope of restoring the ratio. Should the ratio improve, cost cutting is often relaxed and extraneous costs allowed to take root. As a measure of profits, therefore, the ratio of profits to sales does not give management any indication of the part costs play in the generation of profits.

It is not intended here to discuss in any detail methods of measuring return on investment beyond pointing out that they afford manage-

ment a way of controlling costs so that certain functions and departments of the business are not kept from making their full contribution
to profits. For example, where management is using an inadequate
measure of profits, it might drastically reduce the costs of the personnel
department with the idea of adding the amount of the reduction to
gross profits. But this economy might well deprive the department of
skilled interviewers, with unfortunate results for the sales department,
the efficiency of which depends on the recruitment of productive salesmen. Similarly, the costs of the research and development department
might be reduced unreasonably, adversely affecting the company's
product and market position. In other words, undue dependence on
an inadequate measure of profits can obscure the investment nature
of many costs. That is why the notion of cutting costs and expanding
sales is basically fallacious, because many of the costs must be maintained at or above their present level to make profitable sales possible.
At the same time, there are other costs which can be reduced without
impairing the profit-making potential of the firm. A true, adequate,
revealing measure of profits shows that the sought-for residual consists
in more than scattered savings made throughout the company. "False
economy" never had a more exact meaning than when it was applied
in this context.

A management aware of this cost-profits relationship will first decide
which functions or departments are critical to profits before launching
a cost-reduction program. In reality, it will adopt a cost-control program, thereby taking a management view of costs rather than an accounting view. Costs throughout the company will then become related
to the objectives management adopts as a result of settling on profit-
making areas. Department heads, as a result, will be able to coordinate
their activities in an over-all plan. The conflicts that inevitably arise
between departments when the only objective is to meet quotas and
stay within the budget will be resolved.

Profit Objectives

As noted, many functions or departments in a company contribute
to over-all profits. Except in the very smallest firms, these separate
segments operate often on their own initiative with only general guidance from top management. Frequently the only guidance established
by top management for these segments is to meet quotas and stay

within the budget. Even though each function or department might be conscientiously working for the good of the whole company, conflicts can develop which may seriously affect over-all profit performance.

> In an organization each functional unit (division, department, or section) has a part of the whole job to perform. Each part is necessary for the accomplishment of the over-all objectives of the organization. A result of this division of labor, however, is that each functional unit develops objectives of its own. For example, the production department generally assumes the objective of minimizing the cost of production and maximizing production volume. The marketing department tries to minimize the cost of unit sales and maximize sales volume. The finance department attempts to optimize the capital investment policy of the business. The personnel department tries to hire good people at minimum cost, and to retain them, etc. . . .[1]

These conflicts will develop where management fails to exert the proper *profit* planning and control. In other words, no one has decided (1) what elements of the business are most important for their actual or potential contribution to net profits and (2) how to measure these contributions in terms of over-all results. What is needed is a top-management decision on over-all *profit objectives,* with each functional unit of the firm working toward these objectives.

Profit objectives may be defined as goals that management sets up for those functions or departments which are most critical for their actual or potential contribution to the net profits of the firm. In locating these functions or departments and setting goals, management should stand back and look at the company, its resources, the market for its product, and its standing in relation to competitors. Management can even at this stage work out a company philosophy centering on the question: "What are we in business for?" Seeking answers to this question, many managements have been surprised to discover that the company has actually been wasting perfectly good resources and effort on the wrong markets or wrong products.

In setting goals, management gains a clear insight into the essential characteristics of the business and also into the way key functions or departments impinge on each other. Thus, profit objectives can help

[1] C. W. Churchman, R. L. Ackoff, and B. L. Arnoff, *Introduction to Operations Research,* John Wiley & Sons, Inc., New York, 1957.

prevent one function being favored at the expense of others, thereby enabling management to resolve departmental or divisional conflicts.

Consider the elementary case of a manufacturing firm's management deciding that the production and sales departments are most important from a profit standpoint. Management must now decide what can be done to increase the contribution of each department to profits. Consideration of this question takes management into all the

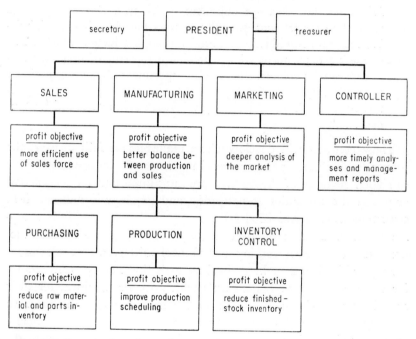

Fig. 1-1. Organization chart of a manufacturing company, showing profit-producing functions and profit objectives.

ramifications of the business, relating every problem to the chosen profit objectives.

Management might find, for example, that the production department's profit contribution would be increased if it adopted better scheduling methods. With such methods, the department could lower the level of raw material and parts inventories, speed up deliveries of finished goods, and decrease inventories of finished goods. Similarly, it might be found that the sales department's contribution to profits could be increased by concentrating more effort on high-profit volume sales, improving coverage of promising markets, and recruiting and training more field salesmen. Each of these recommendations for improving the two departments' contributions to profits becomes a goal or profit objective. The idea of cost reduction per se has remained secondary. Indeed, to achieve some of the objectives (e.g., recruiting and training salesmen), management is willing to increase cost. Thus, the cost has been considered in relation to profit, or as an investment capable of producing profit. The profit objective of better production scheduling, on the other hand, would result in lower unit costs of product and eliminate the pressing inventory problems.

By taking the profit-objective approach, management will also aid in settling conflicts between the sales and production departments. The need for better production scheduling will require closer cooperation between the two departments in aligning production with sales volume and sales patterns. Under conventional budget and quota controls, each department might be tempted to maximize their respective performances regardless of how this might affect the other. Under the profit-objective approach, however, the need of one department becomes the need of the other. Further, the sales data needed for the sales department's marketing plans will also serve as a basis for production department scheduling.

In making a careful choice of profit objectives, management can invariably gain insight into the true nature of the firm's characteristics. The management of a merchandising firm, for example, might view inventories and its sales organization as the two most important contributors to profits. As profit objectives, therefore, management selects tighter inventory control and more profitable sales. If each objective were pursued separately, the tendency would be to reduce excess inventory wherever possible, thus reducing the costs of handling it. Further, the sales manager would attempt to juggle the twin problems of cutting selling expenses and persuading salesmen to spend their time on big-volume customers.

But profit objectives cannot be handled in this way. Since management has already placed some value on the quality of its sales organization, it will wish this talent to be used as efficiently and effectively as possible. It may well find that this asset is, in fact, being squandered by directing it toward high-volume sales. Especially would this be so if the firm's lines included a number of low-profit, low-turnover items. At this stage, management would seriously consider revising the product line to make better use of a good sales organization. Such a revision would, in turn, solve much of the inventory problem and thereby meet the profit objective of tighter inventory control.

The profit-objective approach has been adopted by many companies in recent years. Although it is known by many different names—profit planning, managing by profit centers, profit budgeting, etc.—it is

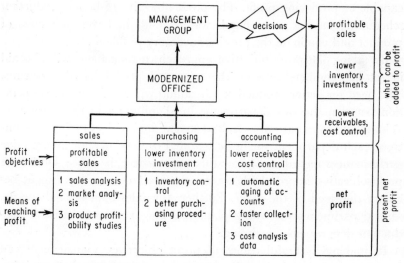

Fig. 1-2. Profit objectives for a merchandising firm.

essentially a means whereby management can establish dynamic goals for the proper planning and control of the business.

Profit Objectives and Data Processing

From the standpoint of punched-card data processing, the setting of profit objectives is imperative for several reasons:

1. *Objectives determine what information management will need from a data processing system.* To attain the objectives it has established, management will require certain records and reports. Particular operating records will be needed to enable all departments and all levels of management to participate in accomplishing the stated objectives. Top management itself will need periodic reports showing progress toward the objectives. Thus, in establishing objectives, management is in effect deciding the firm's data processing requirements.

For example, the management of a firm manufacturing machine units to customers' contract specifications decided on better production control as a principal profit objective. Such control was vital to profits because it would eliminate expensive interruptions in production and also help avoid order cancellations caused by inability to advise customers of firm delivery dates. To meet this objective, management decided that it needed a weekly order-status report to keep it informed on the progress of every job going through the plant. Such a report would show the production position of each order, the date the order was due out of a section, scheduled shipping date, originally assigned shipping date, list and net amount of the order, and job number. Management believed that with such information it could keep customers accurately advised and also schedule purchases of materials and parts to avoid unforeseen shutdowns.

The need for such a report had wide ramifications so far as the firm's current data processing system was concerned. For one thing, it created the need for certain source documents and operating records not then available. For another, it involved combining and summarizing a mass of data from the customer, sales department, engineering department, purchasing department, and other sources. Until it named this objective, management had never been entirely aware of what it could expect of a data processing system.

2. *By establishing objectives, management can appraise the ability of present clerical methods to furnish the required records and reports.* Without objectives, management is in no position to judge the adequacy of its present clerical methods. In the example of the manufacturing company, the need for the weekly order-status reports convinced management that a new data processing system was required. Existing methods were incapable of processing the variety and quantity of data to produce this key report. However, the decision to replace present methods with a new system was not taken until a methods study revealed that the inadequacies were irremediable under current procedures. Objectives will not point up inadequacies in detail, but they will lead management to recognize that they exist.

3. *Objectives determine the emphasis of a data processing system.* Every data processing system, manual or mechanical, reflects to some degree the intentions of management. This is to say that the information management wants *out* of a system determines what data goes *into* the system. The data processing system designed to provide man-

agement with a comprehensive order-status report (as mentioned above) will naturally emphasize data bearing on engineering, parts requirements, production schedules, etc. The same firm could, for equally good profit reasons, decide on more accurate market analysis as an objective, in which case the system would be oriented to processing data relevant to sales, customer buying patterns, seasonal sales patterns, etc. In other words, depending on management's objectives, the data processing system will tend to emphasize particular phases of the firm's operations.

In this connection, it is important that management select the right objectives. Otherwise, it could end up with a system unable to furnish information that is really needed. For example, the sales-minded president of a firm might persuade his management to establish higher sales as a principal objective, although the firm's most pressing need is for better control over production costs. The result can be a data processing system designed around the president's desire for sales figures and consequently incapable of furnishing reliable and detailed cost information.

Similarly, having settled on objectives at the start, management should not suddenly abandon them in favor of new objectives later. Especially is this dangerous after an automatic data processing system has been installed. Although a punched-card system, for example, is highly flexible, it cannot produce records and reports at management's whim. A potentially good system can be made to founder if management never makes up its mind what objectives the system is to serve.

4. *Objectives help define the future data processing requirements of a firm.* In arriving at a decision on profit objectives, management will certainly consider the firm's future prospects. Growth, new products, new markets, competition—these and other factors will influence the choice of objectives. As a consequence, management will be conscious of the need for a system that can grow with the firm and with its data processing requirements.

A parts distributor, for example, set as an objective a closer balance between inventory and sales volume. Investigation revealed that a punched-card system would enable this objective to be reached. However, management wisely studied future sales prospects as well as past sales patterns and found that growth potentials were greater than at first expected. As a result of its findings, it authorized an electronic data processing system that would take care of the firm's data processing requirements for several years to come. Even eighteen months after the system was installed, it was handling 30 per cent more work. Had management not taken growth into consideration, or properly assessed it, it could have installed a system that would soon have been unequal to increased work loads.

5. *Objectives establish the requirements which a new data processing system must satisfy.* Obviously, if present clerical methods are unable to provide the information demanded by the objectives, management is in a position to consider the feasibility of punched cards (or any alternative to present methods). The point is that the over-all profit objectives permit management both to appraise present methods and to judge the effectiveness of a new system. Thus management is given one standard against which to measure both systems; there is not one set of objectives for present procedures and another for punched cards. The objectives set up requirements which one system or the other must fulfill.

What About Clerical Savings?

Although emphasis has been placed here on the importance of the data processing system contributing to the profits of the business, can management not reasonably expect savings to result from the installation of a more efficient data processing system? Many companies that have installed a punched-card data processing system are enjoying many clerical economies. But, in fairness, it should be pointed out that they did not seek these economies in the first instance. They were seeking, rather, decision-making information to improve the over-all profit performance of the firm. Nevertheless, it can also be pointed out that they achieved very substantial savings in the preparation of this vital information. They eliminated all overtime in the preparation of reports and costly inaccuracies due to fatigue, lack of interest, and neglect on the part of employees. Some of them were able to eliminate employees whose abilities were frankly marginal.

But it must be emphasized that, while operating economies in the office are desirable, any savings they produce are inconsequential compared with the additions to the firm's profits that can be made by a management using up-to-date, accurate report data. Generally, it is the case with a firm installing punched-card data processing that, while over-all office cost may remain the same as before, management is actually getting more mileage out of that cost. It is getting more for every dollar spent in the office. Just as $2,500 will today buy more automobile performance than $2,500 spent twenty-five years ago, so will the money spent on a punched-card installation buy more efficiency, speed, accuracy, and report output than the same amount spent on a manual system.

Consequently, what is usually regarded as a by-product of a punched-card system becomes, in fact, the principal purpose of the system. Instead of clerical savings being the main reason for installation of the system, the reports which the system makes available for improved management planning and control become the main reason for converting to newer methods.

2

What Is Data Processing?

The term *data processing* seems to indicate data being subjected to some kind of manufacturing operation during which they are sorted, graded, washed, sliced, diced, cooked, flavored, and canned ready for use. Without forcing the metaphor too far, this is in effect what happens, whether the data are handled by conventional office machines or by punched-card systems. They are put through a series of manipulations which renders them useful or significant to the business. To understand these manipulations, especially when they are carried out by punched cards, it is necessary to clarify some terms. First, the data defined in the following pages are business data (as distinct from scientific or other data) generated by a company's transactions. The term *transactions* is used here to denote all the dealings a company has with customers, vendors, employees, stockholders, and the government and also intracompany dealings among departments and branches of the company. Together, these transactions result in the operating and accounting records and management reports which permit the mass of business data to be recorded, communicated, and acted upon. The interrelationship existing among all these data gives rise to the *total-system approach* necessary to the successful application of punched-card or automatic data processing methods.

17

Data Processing Defined

From the standpoint of a business, *data processing* may be defined as the clerical routine entailed in the preparation of the firm's operating records, accounting records, and management reports.

Operating Records. These consist of the business papers or documents used to record the essential facts of a company's transactions with customers, vendors, employees, stockholders, and the government and also the facts of the firm's internal operations stemming from those transactions. The main purpose of operating records is to enable these facts to be put in such form that they can be understood, communicated, and acted upon. The variety of such records needed in the operation of a firm is huge: payroll records, sales orders, purchase orders, receiving slips, toolroom requisitions, expense vouchers, spoilage slips, move tickets, etc. By means of these records significant data can travel from hand to hand, from department to department, permitting each transaction to be carried out.

FIG. 2-1. Management reports derive from a company's operating and accounting records.

Accounting Records. These include the chart of accounts, journals, ledgers, and periodic statements (trial balance, profit and loss or income statement, and balance sheet) detailing the financial position of the company. Many of the operating records serve as source documents for the accounting functions, e.g., invoice copies, expense vouchers, and vendors' invoices.

Management Reports. These derive from both the operating records and the accounting records. They include statements prepared by the accounting department (such as cost analyses and expense-to-revenue statements), as well as analyses of nonfinancial data (sales analyses, analyses of customers' paying habits, etc.). These reports are not restricted to those prepared exclusively for members of top management but embrace also those needed by all other levels of management and supervision.

Data processing can also be viewed in relation to the main functions of the company. In a manufacturing company, the main functions are production, sales, purchasing, payroll, and accounting. Here are the principal types of records and reports prepared in connection with each function:

Accounting
Chart of accounts
Journals
Ledgers
Financial statements: trial balance, profit and loss, balance sheet, etc.

Sales
Order processing and invoicing
Sales accounting or analysis
Accounts receivable
Cash receiving and credit control

Purchasing
Requisitions, purchase orders, receiving
Purchase and expense distribution
Accounts payable
Cash-paying procedure

Production
Production control
Inventory control
Cost accounting

Payroll
Employment
Timekeeping
Payroll procedure
Payroll distribution

Although they are both alphabetical and numerical, the data used in the preparation of a firm's records and reports are quantitative in character, expressing quantities, prices, periods of time, etc. Excluded from the definition of data processing, therefore, are such clerical routines as letter writing and memorandum writing. Some firms heavily engaged in research and development activities regard data processing as also including the processing of scientific data. In this book, however, the concern is solely with procedures involved in the processing of business or commercial data.

There Are Two Kinds of Data

The sheer variety of data involved in the preparation of a firm's operating records, accounting records, and management reports would seem to defy any attempt at mechanization—if by mechanization is meant applying the mass production idea.

Mass production is made possible by having standard components that can be assembled in a sequence of logical steps. How is it possible to apply this idea to invoicing or payroll or purchasing when every invoice and payroll record and purchase order is unique, containing data pertinent to only one transaction? Ten invoices covering ten sales transactions with ten different customers, for example, seem to have nothing in common with one another. All names and addresses of customers, items ordered, quantities of items ordered, and many other data are different.

Yet running through the data in these invoices and in other operating records are certain broad similarities, which enable these data to be organized for swift, accurate, automatic processing. Because of these similarities, the data are susceptible of broad classification so that they can be handled according to the mass production idea. If the numerical and alphabetical data appearing on an operating record were examined, they would be found to be essentially of two kinds.

Constant Data. This is *reference* or *file* information, which is repeatedly used during the course of a firm's various transactions: names and addresses of customers and suppliers, names of employees, descriptions and prices of items sold and purchased, etc.

Variable Data. This is information which is created by the transaction itself and is unique to that transaction alone: quantity of items ordered by a customer, quantity of items ordered from a vendor, number of hours worked by an employee, etc.

Constant and variable data are combined to produce the desired record. An invoice, for example, is the result of combining data such as the following:

Constant	*Variable*
Customer's name and address	Customer's order number
Customer's industry class	Invoice number
Description of items ordered	Invoice date
Cost and selling prices	Quantity of items ordered
Units of measure	Quantity shipped
Point of shipment	Net weight of shipment
Shipped via	Number of containers
Salesman originating order	Transportation charges
Discount category	

The constant and variable data used to prepare a payroll record would include the following:

Constant	Variable
Employee's name	Hours worked
Clock number	Overtime
Social Security number	Miscellaneous deductions
Hourly rate	Dates
Periodic permanent deductions	
Tax class	

When accumulated for a period, the combined constant and variable data appearing in a number of similar records can be rearranged

---

CONSOLIDATED DISTRIBUTORS, INC.
FORT LEE, NEW YORK

608

INVOICE TO
AUTO SERVICE, INC.
123 NORTH BROADWAY
NEW YORK, NEW YORK

TERMS
2/10 NET 30

608

SHIP TO
AUTO SERVICE, INC.
123 NORTH BROADWAY
NEW YORK, NEW YORK

TRUCK DELIVER BEFORE 9 A.M.				17323	7 12 5	35182
SHIPPING INSTRUCTIONS				ORDER NO.	DATE	INVOICE NO.

STOCK NO.	DESCRIPTION	UNIT	QUANTITY	UNIT PRICE	AMOUNT
212526	BEARING PILOT	EA	12	.55	6.60
429739	TRANSMISSION CASE	EA	1	34.25	34.25
453812	GASKET-VALVE COVER	EA	12	1.30	15.60
506380	SEAL OIL FRONT WHEEL	EA	15	.745	11.18
507676	CRANKSHAFT	EA	1	89.45	89.45
630035	BEARING MAIN	EA	3	4.50	13.50
630546	PISTON	EA	6	12.60	75.60
773323	FILTER OIL	EA	6	11.92	71.52
807204	CARBURETOR ASSEMBLY	EA	1	78.50	78.50
814959	TRANSMISSION ASSEMBLY	EA	1	375.00	375.00
	GROSS INVOICE AMOUNT				771.20
	5 PER CENT DISCOUNT				38.56
	3 PER CENT SALES TAX				21.98
	INVOICE TOTAL				754.62

FIG. 2-2. Constant and variable data on an invoice. The boxed portions are constant or file data, and the shaded portions are variable data created by this single transaction with a customer. The remaining data are the extended items and totals resulting from combining the constant and variable data.

or grouped in report form. A report showing the month's sales of a particular item, for instance, would consist of some of the combined constant and variable data appearing in the invoices for the same period.

There Are Four Processing Steps

Opinions keep proliferating as to the number of processing steps needed to combine constant and variable data to produce records and reports. The accountant, thinking strictly in terms of his own accounting records, has long recognized three such steps: (1) *recording* data in the journals, (2) *classifying* data by posting them to the ledgers, and (3) *summarizing* the accounts in report or statement form.

With the evolution of mechanized data processing, these terms have been borrowed and their meaning widened to describe clerical operations of a nonaccounting, as well as an accounting, nature. To them has been added *calculating,* to recognize the use of automatic data processing units possessing computing ability. As a result, the new terminology of data processing defines the four main processing steps as follows:

Recording: Both constant and variable data must be recorded in some form so that they can be worked with. The recording can consist in handwriting, typewriting, punched holes in cards or tape, or magnetic spots on tape or disks.

Classifying: This is the grouping of similar items prior to accumulating and printing totals for these items in report form. A report showing the total monthly sales of each salesman requires that all items sold during the month be classified by salesman.

Summarizing: The final record or report summarizes in written form the data pertinent to one transaction or group of transactions. A record such as an invoice shows who has bought an item, where it has been shipped, the terms of payment, the total amount charged, etc. A report such as an aged trial balance summarizes the status of each account receivable.

Calculating: Multiplication, division, addition, or subtraction of certain of the numerical data is necessary to obtain a result reflecting the transaction. A payroll check results from a series of calculations involving such constant data as the employee's hourly rate and tax class and such variable data as the numbers of hours he worked during the pay period.

Some authorities suggest adding a fifth processing step—*reporting*—to indicate the printing of a final record or report, for, they contend, summarizing inadequately describes this phase of data processing.

In the case of computers, there are considered to be three processing steps: *input* (recording and feeding data into the computer), *processing* (which includes manipulation and computing), and *output* (the final result in the form of punched cards or tape, magnetic tape, or printed records and reports).

The Paperwork Pyramid

The multitude of data involved in the many clerical operations in a business interrelate with one another in countless ways. For example, the data involved in sales order processing are related to such clerical procedures as inventory control, production control, sales analysis, and accounting. Similarly, the data involved in inventory control interrelate with data involved in purchasing procedures. Purchasing procedures create data that become involved in production control. Thus, all the data generated by a firm's transactions and by the operations stemming from those transactions impinge on each other at some time during the course of the firm's business day. The effect of this interrelating of data is to build a paperwork pyramid that can become quite formidable, depending on how the data are processed.

What inflates the paperwork pyramid is the repetition of various of the processing steps. If, to maintain the interrelationships which inevitably occur between and among the firm's many transactions, data must be continually re-recorded at each stage of processing, the pyramid becomes broader and deeper. In manual processing, this re-recording or recopying of data at each stage is caused by the fact that they become entangled with one another in the various operating records. Before certain sales order data can be used for production scheduling purposes, for instance, they must be extracted from invoice copies and grouped according to some sequence or period. This means that another stratum is added to the paperwork pyramid as clerks comb through the invoice copies isolating the required data.

The paperwork pyramid can cast a dark shadow, discouraging management's attempts at securing transaction analysis for improved control and planning. With manual office methods, the pyramid stands squarely in the way of reports essential to effective management decisions. Consequently, such reports are prepared only intermittently, when management's situation becomes desperate enough to demand

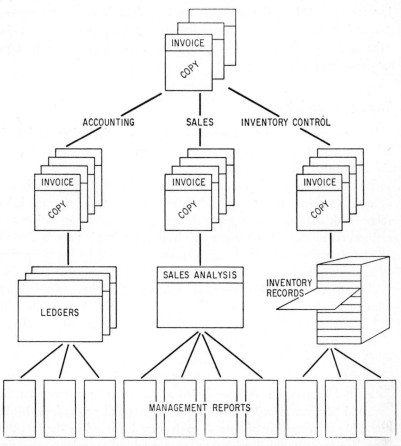

Fig. 2-3. The paperwork pyramid, showing the multiplication of paperwork effort occasioned by the need to recopy constant data at each stage of processing.

them. The conventional office is, therefore, frequently given over to sudden rushes of work to provide "crash" analyses of payroll, accounts receivable, or other such reports.

To escape from the crushing weight of the paperwork pyramid, many businesses have turned to punched-card processing. As will be

shown in the next chapter, the punched-card method of data processing eliminates effectively the two principal reasons for the pyramid's
existence: continual reprocessing of data and the burying of significant
data in copies of operating records. By keeping various kinds of data
always separate from one another, and thus quickly retrievable,
punched-card data processing removes the roadblock to clerical efficiency which is represented by the soaring paperwork pyramid.

The Total-system Approach

In the very fact that data interrelate with one another can be found
a principle that should govern management's attitude to data processing. This principle can be labeled the *total-system approach,* meaning
that data processing should be regarded not as a collection of isolated
clerical procedures but rather as a system able to integrate these
various procedures. Thus, although there may be many procedures,
each is, in fact, linked with the others, just as the firm's various functions and departments are linked together.

A Remington Rand publication states that a typical company is
"composed of myriad channels through which money and material
flow in fulfillment of the company's obligations to its customers, vendors, employees, stockholders, and the government." This view of a
company clearly implies interconnections among the various functions
and departments. And instrumental to the flow of money and material
is the flow of data. Just as there is an interconnection between the
various departments, so is there a total system embracing its clerical
functions. This total-system principle can apply whether manual
methods or mechanized methods are being used. The difference lies
in the degree to which the various clerical functions are integrated
with one another. As noted earlier, manual methods create a paperwork pyramid that, although it may slow the flow of data, never
completely obstructs it. If complete obstruction occurred, any communication within the company would be quite impossible.

If it seems that an obvious point is being labored here, it should be
pointed out that it is the inability of many managements to grasp the
total-system principle which prevents them from fully appreciating
the benefits of automatic data processing—or, indeed, the importance
of data processing itself to management objectives.

The benefits of automatic methods—punched cards, for example—

lie in the fact that they can turn data interrelationships to the advantage of the firm, and thus of management. These methods exploit the fact that data employed in a procedure such as invoicing will be reused in other procedures, such as inventory control, production control, or report preparation. They do so by furnishing the link that integrates one procedure with another; the link is the punched card,

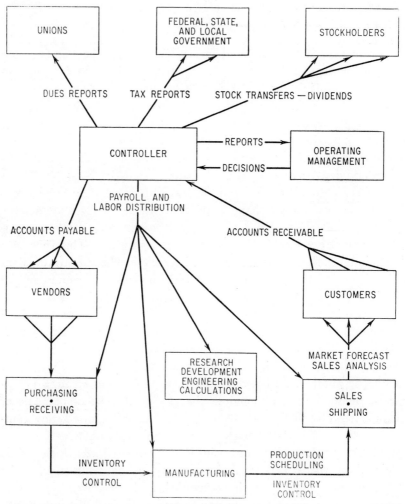

Fig. 2-4. Total system. Schematic showing the interrelating of data processing areas in a typical manufacturing firm. (*Remington Rand Univac.*)

punched tape, or magnetic tape, which automatically instructs various data processing machines how to handle the data it contains.

This ability of automatic methods to link previously scattered procedures is well expressed in a recent definition of data processing: "The manipulation of pre-determined input data in the form of pre-determined outputs." This definition could be reworded to read "the manipulation of *operating records and accounting records* in the form of predetermined *management reports.*" Explicit in this modified definition is an idea that is now axiomatic in data processing—namely, that what is desired out of any given system (manual or automatic)

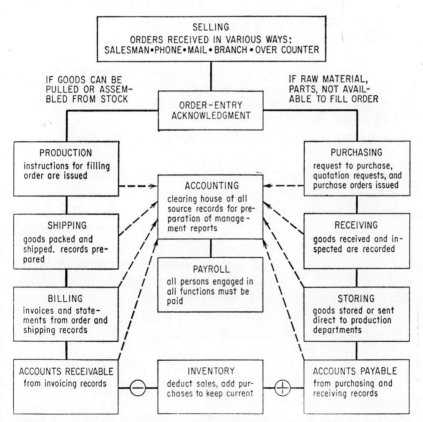

PAPERWORK AND THE BASIC FUNCTIONS OF BUSINESS

Fig. 2-5. Another conception of the total-system idea. (*Standard Register Company.*)

depends on what goes into the system. But this idea will escape a management unwilling, unready, or unable to adopt the total-system approach to data processing in its firm.

Those who have specialized in the study of systems and procedures in business have long been aware of data interrelationships. Because of their work, a foundation has been laid for great progress in automatic data processing. One of the cases in this book (page 201) describes how American Bosch Division has applied what IBM calls the *management operating system* (MOS) to its manufacturing control functions. IBM's explanation of MOS reveals the total-system approach as being entirely practicable:

> The basis of the management operating system is the interaction of the basic manufacturing control functions which generate all plant activity. For example, sales forecasting produces a finished product plan as machine output which, in turn, is entered as input for materials planning. When passed against bills of material . . . the finished product plan produces total materials requirements. Materials requirements are checked against inventory . . . to initiate purchases and manufacturing orders. This chain of events, which is set in motion each time customer orders are entered into the system, continues through scheduling, dispatching, and finally through operations evaluation.

By recognizing that the output of one procedure becomes the input of another, this firm has successfully applied the total-system approach.

In adopting this approach, management will soon realize the economic value of data processing. In general, the true value of data processing is measured in the information it yields for improved control and planning. This information derives from operating and accounting records. If management is indifferent to the direct relationship existing between these records and between these records and management reports, it will be unable to encourage the installation of a system that can contribute to the profitable operation of the business.

3

The Punched Card

Possibly everyone has faced the job of putting a long written list of names in alphabetical order. One way to rearrange them is to number the names in the proper order and copy them to a new sheet. Another way is to copy the names onto cards and then sort the cards alphabetically. This last method illustrates very simply punched-card data processing. For the essential idea behind punched cards is to get data into such form that they are readily accessible for various purposes. This idea is hardly new. To get back to the written list of names, even the smallest business would hardly keep its customer list in this form. Rather it will maintain a file of index cards so that, for example, certain names can be easily withdrawn for addressing direct mail. Like the index card, the punched card is a *unit record* containing one kind of data, which can be combined with other kinds of data punched in other cards. The main reason why the data are *punched* into the cards is to enable them to be processed mechanically.

The Punched Card

The holes in a punched card do double duty. First, they hold in coded form the constant and variable data to be processed. Second, the same holes allow electric or mechanical contacts to be made within each of the various punched-card machines. These contacts actuate a machine to handle the card's punched data in a certain way, depending on how the machine is set, or wired. A sorter, for example, can be set so that contacts through certain holes will cause a number of cards to be arranged in some desired sequence. A reproducing punch can be wired through its control panel to punch all the data appearing in one card into another card; or it can be wired to punch only part of the data into the other card.

International Business Machines Corporation describes the double-duty nature of the punched hole in this way:

> The punched hole will add itself to something else, subtract itself from something else, multiply itself by something else, divide itself into something else, list itself, reproduce itself, classify itself, select itself, print itself on a card, produce an automatic balance forward, file itself, post itself, cause a total to be printed, compare itself to something else, reproduce and print itself on the end of a card, cause a form to feed to a predetermined position, or to be rejected automatically, or to space the form from one position to another.

Because they must actuate complex, sensitive machines, punched cards are manufactured to exacting standards and of a special grade of paper, which will withstand the effects of frequent manual handling. Nevertheless, cards should be carefully handled and protected from dust, moisture, extreme temperature changes, or any influence that would impair their function.

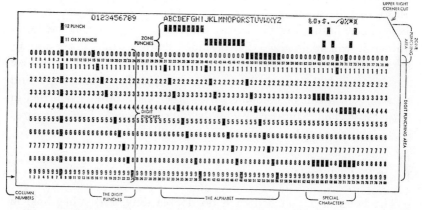

FIG. 3-1. IBM punched card. This card carries data in the form of rectangular holes in 80 vertical columns. A number is represented by one hole, an alphabetical character by two. (*International Business Machines Corporation.*)

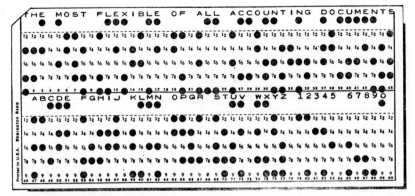

Fig. 3-2. Remington Rand card. Data appear in this card as round holes in 45 columns divided horizontally into two fields for a total of 90 columns. Both numbers and letters require two holes. (*Remington Rand Univac.*)

The two main types of punched cards in widest use today are made by the two leading manufacturers of punched-card equipment, International Business Machines Corporation and Remington Rand Division, Sperry Rand Corporation. Neither of these two types of cards is compatible with the other. IBM cards can be used only with IBM machines or machines designed to accept them. The same is true of Remington Rand cards.

The IBM card is distinguishable by its rectangular holes and 80-column format. There is a total of 12 punching positions in each column, the eleventh and twelfth positions (the two rows running across the top edge of the card) being called the X and Y punches, respectively, which are often used for special machine instructions. A numeral requires one hole in a column, an alphabetical character two holes.

In the Remington Rand card, data are recorded in the form of round holes punched in 45 columns. These columns are divided horizontally into two areas of six punching positions per column, so there is a total of 90 columns in the card. Numerical and alphabetical punches each require two holes per digit or character.

Many different designs of cards have come into use: checks, vouchers, statements with or without stubs attached, and even addressing stencils. IBM has developed a *mark sense card* on which information can be marked with a graphite pencil and later automatically converted to punched holes by a machine sensing the pencil marks. As

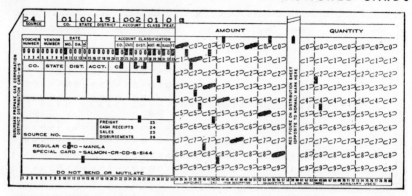

FIG. 3-3. IBM mark sense card enables data to be recorded as pencil marks in spaces at right. These marks are later automatically converted to holes by a punch that senses the pencil marks. (*International Business Machines Corporation.*)

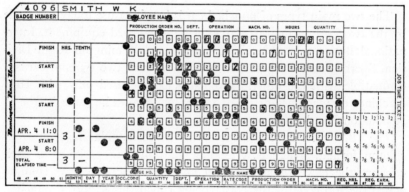

FIG. 3-4. Remington Rand has a similar card. Penciled marks are automatically read by an optical scanning punch and converted into holes. (*Remington Rand Univac.*)

the use of punched-card systems grows, the number and variety of punched cards will assuredly increase.

The Punched Card as a Unit Record

The flexibility of a punched-card installation derives not only from the versatility of the various machines but also from the *unit-record* principle governing the placing of data in the cards. Only one unit of information is recorded in a punched card; that is, the card will contain only data that remain *permanently* together through all stages of processing.

Thus, the constant and variable data used in preparing an invoice must be recorded in several cards. There would be, for example, *customer master cards* punched only with data permanently associated with one customer. One card would contain the customer's name, another his street address, and another his city address. All cards would be punched with the customer's account number, and possibly also with a salesman's code number and an industry classification code number. (Frequently, all these data pertaining to one customer can be punched in one master card.)

For constant data relating to each item ordered by a customer, there would be a *product master card* punched with description, code number, size, package unit, cost and selling prices, etc. Other constant data —terms of payment, shipped via, etc.—would be punched in other master cards. There would also be master cards containing constant data used in the preparation of reports: name of salesman, names of branches, etc.

The variable data relating to a particular sales transaction between a firm and its customer would be punched into separate cards. The quantity of an item ordered would be recorded in an *item detail card* along with relevant constant data reproduced from the customer, product, and other master cards. Other variable data, such as the customer's order number, would be punched in separate cards.

All the cards containing these several units of constant and variable data are then combined to print out the required invoice; yet each unit of data remains available for reuse in the preparation of other records and reports.

Punched-card methods speed up data processing because the constant data can be *prepunched* in master cards and held in files ready for use when required. At the time a batch of the day's orders is to be processed, therefore, only the variable data need be recorded or punched at that time. The constant data, in the form of master cards, can then be immediately withdrawn from the files and brought together with the variable data for processing. This procedure saves considerable time, since it has been estimated that up to 90 per cent of the data used in preparing operating records such as invoices is repetitive or constant.

As unit records, punched cards are especially useful for summariz-

CONSTANT DATA

VARIABLE DATA

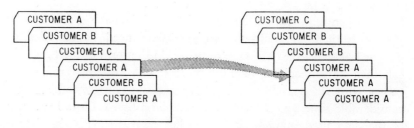

FILE OF CUSTOMER MASTER CARDS

on each card:
customer's name, address
customer account number
industry class
salesman code number

CUSTOMER CARD

FILE OF PRODUCT MASTER CARDS

on each card:
item description
item code number
cost, selling prices

ITEM DETAIL CARD ← quantity ordered / quantity shipped

MISCELLANEOUS DATA CARD ← customer's order number / invoice number / terms / date of order / date shipped

SHIPPING DATA CARD ← shipping instructions

FREIGHT CHARGES ← freight charges

WORKING DECK

Fig. 3-5. The unit-record idea reserves separate cards for separate groups of data being processed. When run through a tabulating or accounting machine, these cards, combined into a working deck, will actuate the machine to print out an invoice.

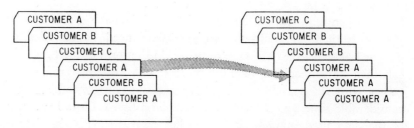

CUSTOMER A
CUSTOMER B
CUSTOMER C
CUSTOMER A
CUSTOMER B
CUSTOMER A

CUSTOMER C
CUSTOMER B
CUSTOMER B
CUSTOMER A
CUSTOMER A
CUSTOMER A

Fig. 3-6. *Sorting* is grouping cards in some sequence according to any classification punched in them. Above, cards have been arranged alphabetically by customer by sorting on customers' account numbers.

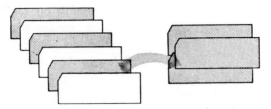

Fig. 3-7. *Selecting* is pulling certain cards (such as those punched with a particular date) from a number of other cards.

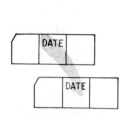

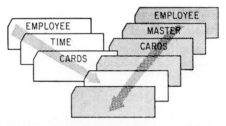

Fig. 3-8. *Duplicating* is the automatic punching of repetitive data from a master card into one or more succeeding cards.

Fig. 3-9. *Merging* combines two sets of punched cards into one set of a given sequence. Above, employee timecards are merged with matching master cards.

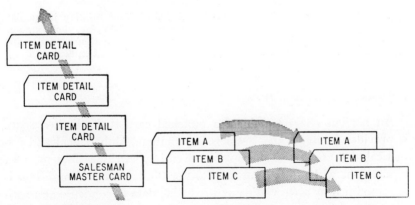

Fig. 3-10. *Gang-punching* is the automatic copying of punched data (such as a salesman's number) into one or more detail cards following it.

Fig. 3-11. *Matching* is a checking function performed automatically by machine. It is frequently performed in conjunction with merging (see Figure 3-9).

ing transactions in report form. The various data connected with each transaction are always kept separate from one another. In contrast, conventional manual methods result in the constant and variable data becoming intermingled with one another in the same records, as in a file of invoice copies. The data are consequently difficult to disentangle and use separately for analysis purposes. Punched cards keep data always "above the surface," always accessible.

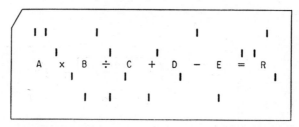

FIG. 3-12. *Calculating* is the computing of a result by multiplying, dividing, or adding, or subtracting factors punched in a card or series of cards and automatically punched in each card or trailer cards.

FIG. 3-13. *Interpreting* is the translation of punched holes into printed information on the face of the card. It is used to make the card easier to identify.

FIG. 3-14. *End printing* is translating punched data into bold printed characters on the end of a card so that it can be identified when filed vertically.

Recording Data in Cards

An obvious characteristic of a punched card is the limited space it provides for recording business information. Alphabetical and numerical data ordinarily occupying several typewritten lines must be made to fit within the confines of 80 or 90 narrow columns. This is accomplished by abbreviating and reducing data to condensed numerical codes wherever possible. The general principles of coding are discussed later in Chapter 9.

Less obvious is the manner in which data are arranged in a punched card. A look at a typical card reveals that the data are punched in vertical columns. Each of these columns is called a *field* and is reserved for particular data: invoice number, customer's name, part number, price, etc. The arrangement of these fields on a card constitutes what is known as *card design*. Because their data processing requirements differ, no two firms will adopt identical card designs. At the same time,

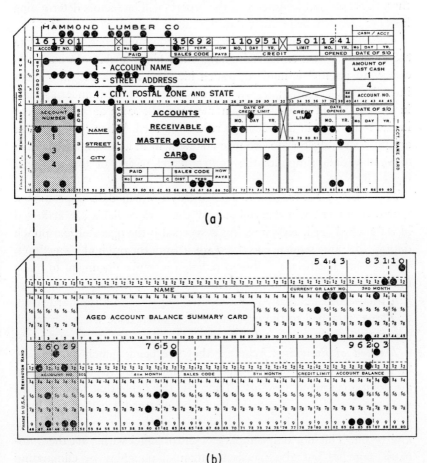

(a)

(b)

FIG. 3-15. Identical data that appear in different cards are usually punched in the same field, or position, in the cards. This simplifies machines operation. The name and account number data appear in the same fields in the summary card (*b*) as they do in the master name card (*a*). (*Remington Rand Univac.*)

they will be governed by the same basic considerations in the design of their cards. Although the actual detail of card design demands the ingenuity of a trained machine accounting supervisor, the basic considerations should be understood by management.

Report Requirements. What comes out of a punched-card system in the way of final reports depends on the data entering the system. Consequently, report requirements must be constantly kept in mind to ensure that the necessary data is recorded in the input cards. Further, the form and frequency of the reports will be factors determining how the data will be positioned in the cards.

Columns in Other Cards. Since cards containing one kind of data are combined with cards containing other kinds of data during processing, an attempt is made to punch identical data in the same fields in each card. For example, where a customer account number appears in a certain field in a customer name card, the same data will appear in the same field in the accounts receivable card. When the two cards are processed together to produce a statement of account, the aligning of similar data simplifies the control-panel wiring of the machines involved.

Sequence of Source Data. The order in which data appear on a source document will determine how the various fields are arranged in a punched card. Keypunching is speeded if the operator can punch data in the same sequence as she reads it from the original. Sometimes, where it has not been possible to redesign a source document to make the sequence of its data correspond to that on a card, the data are first transcribed manually in the desired sequence to a standard form, or *apron,* attached to the original. This is often done when keypunch operators are recording from the original orders sent in by customers.

Method of Punching. Whether they are being punched manually or automatically, card fields that are punched by the same method are usually grouped together. Thus, all the fields that are punched manually on the card punch would be grouped together, all those gang-punched would be grouped together, all those summary-punched, and so on. This not only simplifies control-panel wiring on the automatic punches but also speeds up manual punching by eliminating the need to skip fields.

Types of Information. Generally, all constant and variable data appearing in punched cards are of three kinds: (1) reference, (2) classification, and (3) quantitative. Because of the operating requirements of the various machines, each kind of data has its preferred position on a card: reference information (which identifies the original source, such as an invoice number, batch number, or date) is placed to the left of a card; classification information (account number, commodity code, state, or other information used to prepare summaries) is placed in the center; and quantitative information (unit price, quantity, sales amount) is placed to the right.

Branching out from each of these main considerations are numerous detailed considerations affecting card design. These have to do mainly with the operating characteristics of the various machines, however, and do not alter the basic principles cited above.

What About Exceptions?

Punched-card data processing makes use of the mass production idea, or the assembling of standard components in a sequence of orderly steps. The components, of course, are the punched cards containing constant and variable data, and the steps are those of recording, classifying, calculating, summarizing, and reporting. In keeping with the mass production idea, the efficiency of a punched-card system is highest when it is processing data in quantity. Thus, like transaction and operating data are processed in batches to obtain the greatest benefits from mechanized methods. A number of incoming customer orders, for example, would be allowed to accumulate into a workable batch so that the pulling of master cards from files, keypunching, and other steps in the billing procedure could be carried out at one time.

The mention of mass production in connection with office routine immediately raises the question: What about exceptions? In any business, there is a certain amount of paperwork which departs from the usual pattern: typing out six copies of an invoice for a special customer, an unusual back-order procedure, or a peculiar credit-checking procedure. Management can be expected to ask how such exceptions can possibly be handled on punched cards.

The answer is that many exceptions cannot be handled by the punched-card system but should be handled separately. If the number of exceptions is inordinately high, management may be justified in turning down the conversion to punched cards. But before it does so, management should determine exactly what proportion of its present data processing methods consists of exceptions. Under manual methods, there is an opportunity for exceptions to breed, even though they are not strictly exceptions. By their very nature, manual methods encourage minor departures from established routine. It is easy for the sales manager to ask that orders for an important account be handled in a particular way, or for the credit manager to set up special credit-checking procedures for certain customers, or even for a vendor to demand the use of a special purchase order procedure. Before long, all these cases of special treatment have proliferated into countless and varying exceptions.

What is often overlooked is that an exceptional procedure invariably outlives its need. The customer who once asked for six invoice copies can now get along with three. The customer whom the sales manager once thought required special attention has long forgotten the delayed delivery that made the special attention necessary. So it goes with most exceptions: many of them should never have been started and, once started, were tolerated too long.

Rather than assume that the mass production idea of punched cards cannot be applied to the firm's data processing, management should first find out how many of the present exceptions are really routine procedures that have been allowed to get out of hand.

4

Punched-card Equipment

The equipment that processes the data contained in punched cards ranges from the standard *tab units* to the more complex computers. The units included in the group of standard punched-card machines are mainly electromechanical in function (some advanced units are electronic) and capable of performing the various processing steps. The versatility with which the different machines can carry out these steps is made possible through *control panels,* which are individually wired for each machine.

Because they are becoming more feasible for many kinds of business, computers with punched-card input and output deserve some attention. Computers are self-contained data processing systems that handle data through a system of vacuum tubes, transistors, etc. Fundamentally, the logic they employ in processing data is little different from that of standard punched-card machines, but the fact that they process data electronically gives them an enormous advantage in speed and in the ability to handle large numbers of variables.

The Equipment Classified

A punched-card system consists of the punched card itself and of the machines, or hardware, which act upon the card's instructions.

There are four main groups of machines associated with punched-card data processing, as follows:

1. *Standard Punched-card Machines*
     Manual recording units
        Card punches
        Verifiers
     Automatic recording units
        Reproducing punches
        Summary punches
     Classifying units
        Sorters
        Collators
     Calculating units
        Calculating punches
     Printing units
        Interpreters
        Accounting (or tabulating) machines
2. *Common-language Machines*
        Typewriters: tape-reading, tape-producing, card-reading, card-producing
        Bookkeeping machines: tape-producing, card-producing
        Adding machines: tape-producing
        Communication units
3. *Conversion Units*
        Tape-to-card converters
        Card-to-tape converters
        Tag-to-card converters
        Card-to-card converters
        Paper tape-to-magnetic tape converters
4. *Computers*

Common-language machines are part of the punched-card family inasmuch as their punched-paper-tape output must be converted to punched card to obtain analyses of transactions. The typewriters and other machines producing punched-card output could actually be classed as recording units under Standard Punched-card Machines; to avoid confusion, however, they will be described in this chapter as part of the common-language group.

Standard Punched-card Machines

The machines in this group are basic to a punched-card installation. To an extent, the functions of some overlap the functions of others, so that a satisfactory installation can be made up using only

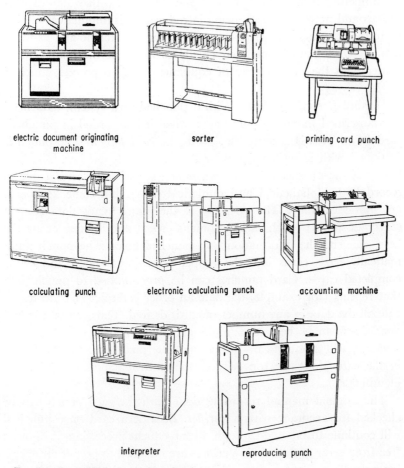

electric document originating machine   sorter   printing card punch

calculating punch   electronic calculating punch   accounting machine

interpreter   reproducing punch

FIG. 4-1. Some IBM punched-card units.

some of the machines. A minimum installation would consist of a card punch, a sorter, and an accounting or tabulating machine; depending on the application and requirements of the business, a reproducing punch (and/or a summary punch), a calculating punch, a collator, and an interpreter might be required in addition.

The machines are manufactured by International Business Machines Corporation and Remington Rand Division, Sperry Rand Corporation. They may be rented or purchased. Accessory equipment (files and cabinets for cards, work tables, etc.) must be purchased.

Because of the variety of machines made by the two companies, the numerous technical differences, and the speed with which modifications and new models are being introduced, it is impractical to give more than a general description of each type of machine and its function. What follows is intended chiefly to acquaint the management reader with the main classes of equipment used to process punched cards.

Manual Recording Units. With a punched-card system, data need be transcribed manually only once: when it is recorded in punched-card form. This is accomplished with the *card punch*. The punch is equipped with a keyboard similar to that on a typewriter. The keyboard of the most commonly used punch is *alphanumerical* (able to record both alphabetical and numerical data), but some keyboards are numerical only. The operator of the punch reads data from a source document (such as a customer's order) and, by depressing the keys, converts the information into punched holes. The punch automatically feeds cards into the proper punching position and stacks completed cards. Card punches can be *programmed* to punch data that repeats (for example, the date an order is received) or to duplicate all the data in any number of cards desired. Thus, actual manual operations can be held to a minimum. Some models, called *printing punches,* will automatically print (or "interpret") the punched data in the card along the top edge of the card, making the card easily identifiable.

The original manual recording done with the card punch can be checked for accuracy with a *verifier.* Because a card once punched will continue to be used through all subsequent processing, it must be free from error of any kind. Verifiers are designed to permit an operator actually to repeat the original punching action on an identical keyboard. The verifier will automatically signal when an error is discovered and indicate its location on the card. There are, of course, other methods of checking card-punching accuracy without using a verifier: reading the printed interpretation on a card, running the cards through a tabulating machine and proofreading the printed result, balancing to predetermined totals which have been set up in controls, zero balancing, etc.

Automatic Recording Units. Once punched cards have entered processing, data must often be transferred from one type of card to another or from one set of cards to another.

The *reproducing punch* performs this recording automatically. It will reproduce a whole new set of master cards for use in processing, enabling the original master cards to be returned to the file for reuse. It will gang-punch certain data from a master card into a number of detail cards; for example, unit price is gang-punched from a product master card into a detail card containing the quantity of items ordered. Ordinarily, this is done in multiple quantities of detail cards. The reproducing punch can also automatically compare data being copied from card to card and signal errors.

The *document-originating machine* is an IBM unit that does all that a reproducing punch will do but, in addition, converts punched data in a card into bold printing across the end of the same card or of another card. On an employee's timecard, for example, this unit will print his clock number. The card, when filed on end, can thus be identified. Both this unit and the IBM reproducing punch (described above) can be fitted with a mark-sensing device to convert pencil marks on a card to punched holes.

Remington Rand has introduced an *optical scanning punch,* which reads and automatically punches a 90-column card marked with penciled strokes, circles, check marks, X's, or the number itself. As long as the mark is placed in the proper position, it will be read and punched as the number represented by that position. The card used with the scanning punch is illustrated in the previous chapter.

An essential automatic recording operation is *summary punching.* It is performed by a document-originating machine (in the case of an IBM installation) or by special summary punches, which may or may not include other functions. The purpose of summary punching is to punch automatically a card that contains totals or summary data pertinent to a particular transaction or group of transactions. These summary cards, representing a condensation or reduction in the volume of the original data, can then be used for preparing a periodic report. Summary punching is performed simultaneously as an accounting machine or tabulator is printing a record or report. As a payroll register is being printed, for example, a summary-punching unit will punch cards with year-to-date data for each entry on the register. Another example of summary punching is the accounts receivable card containing condensed invoice data.

Classifying Units. Depending on the record or report being prepared, the punched cards must be rearranged in a particular sequence,

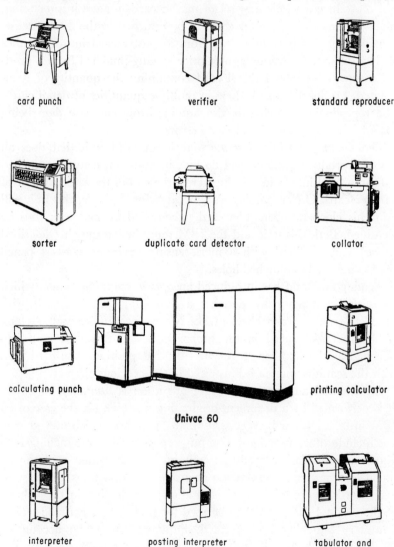

card punch   verifier   standard reproducer

sorter   duplicate card detector   collator

calculating punch   printing calculator

Univac 60

interpreter   posting interpreter   tabulator and
                                                                                summary punch

FIG. 4-2. Some Remington Rand punched-card units.

or certain cards selected or segregated from a number of other cards, or some cards merged or collated or matched with other cards. These manipulations can be quickly handled by two automatic units.

Sorters group cards automatically in numerical or alphabetical sequence according to the data punched in them. For example, cards containing product data can be arranged in customer account number sequence by sorting them on account numbers. The sorter can also select cards punched with specific data (such as a date) from a number of other cards. The sorter mechanism passes cards under an electric brush or photoelectric cell, which is set to search for a particular hole in a particular column. In as many passes as there are digits in the code number being sought, the sorter will deposit the desired cards in one of a series of receptacles or pockets. Depending on its capacity, a sorter can handle other functions; a high-speed electronic sorter, for example, will print a statistical report simultaneously as it sorts.

The *collator* has often been called the "automatic file clerk" of a punched-card system. It feeds two files of punched cards arranged in the same sequence and either matches or merges them on similar data or both. At the same time, the machine will also check the sequence of the cards. Cards containing data that do not match with those in other cards can be automatically selected from either file. An example of merging is bringing each of a file of employees' timecards together with its matching earnings-to-date card.

Calculating Units. High-speed *calculating punches* have been developed that will multiply, divide, add, and subtract several factors punched in one card and punch the result into the same card or into other cards. Such units have the ability to perform the several calculations involved in working out an hourly employee's pay after taxes and deductions, usually with only one pass of the cards through the machine.

Printing Units. The final step in punched-card data processing is the printing of records and reports.

The *tabulator* (or *accounting machine,* or *printer*) prints a variety of records and reports from punched cards: invoices, registers, sales analyses, lists, payroll checks, etc. Besides printing alphabetical and numerical data punched in the cards, the unit will add or subtract to print any combination of totals. Through its control panel, it can be wired to print any record or report using all or part of the data punched in the cards. The machine carriage automatically positions forms for printing; some carriages control the feeding of two different sizes and types of continuous forms at the same time. Single forms

processing step	machine	what it does
MANUAL RECORDING	card punch	enables operator to manually transcribe data from source documents into punched-card form
	verifier	enables operator to check accuracy of original punching; machine automatically signals errors
AUTOMATIC RECORDING	reproducing punch	automatically transfers punched data from one card to another, or from one set of cards to another
	document-originating machine	an IBM unit which, in addition to performing reproducing-punch functions, converts punched data into bold printing across end of card. also converts penciled marks on "mark sense" cards into punched holes
	optical scanning	Remington Rand unit which converts penciled marks into punched holes
CLASSIFYING	sorter	groups cards automatically in numerical or alphabetical sequence according to data punched in them
	collator	merges and/or matches two sets of cards which are in same sequence
CALCULATING	calculating punch	automatically multiplies, divides, adds, subtracts factors punched in card and punches result
PRINTING	tabulator or accounting machine	prints records and reports from punched cards and adds or subtracts to print any combination of totals
	interpreter	prints data punched in card on card itself

FIG. 4-3. Data processing functions performed by standard punched-card units.

and records in card form (e.g., checks) can also be printed by some models. Advanced models of the tabulator can store information for reuse. A summary punch (see above), when connected electrically to the tabulator, will punch cards containing a condensation of the data being printed by the tabulator.

The *interpreter* prints, or interprets, data punched in a card on the card itself. This is often necessary so that a card can be quickly identified. Customer, product, and other master cards containing constant data and held in tub files are usually interpreted so that they can be located and pulled for processing. Interpreting is also a way of checking the accuracy of card punching. An interpreter is often used to print the amount of a check, where the punched card itself is serving as the check. Sometimes an interpreter is used to post the status of a current account on an accounts receivable card.

Common-language Machines

Paralleling the development of punched-card systems has been the appearance of *common-language machines*. Originally, the term *common language* was applied to units actuated by or producing punched paper tape: typewriters, bookkeeping machines, adding machines, etc. Since their introduction, many of these units now accept and emit data in punched-card form. While "common language" could accurately describe the function of punched cards in relation to their own family of standard units described in the previous section, the term has a somewhat special meaning when applied to its own class of equipment.

Common-language units possess this special characteristic: they record original data *at their point of origin* in mechanical form. Thus, using an electric typewriter, an operator can type a record manually and the typewriter will produce automatically a punched tape or card containing in coded form the data typed. This characteristic of the typewriter gave rise to the original definition of the term *integrated data processing*. In punched-card data processing, on the other hand, data originate first as a manually written record and are subsequently recorded manually in punched-card form.

Punched paper tape was first developed for sending data over a distance by telegraph. The tape used for this purpose contained five rows of punched round holes running the length of the tape. Like the holes in a punched card, the holes in punched tape enabled electric circuits to be closed, thereby causing a series of electric impulses to be sent over the telegraph line. It was not until 1950 that Commercial Controls Corporation (now a division of Friden Corporation) introduced an electric typewriter using five-channel punched tape as a data carrying and actuating medium. Since then, bookkeeping machines, adding machines, calculating machines, and cash registers have joined the punched-tape family and also the punched-card family. Also, tape with six, seven, and eight rows of holes has come into use. The latter, developed by IBM, contains in the extra holes a self-checking feature to maintain accuracy and to provide additional electric impulses for printing upper- and lower-case characters.

Fig. 4-4. Common-language Type-   Fig. 4-5. Tape-producing adding
writer. (*Friden Corporation.*)   machine. (*Friden Corporation.*)

Many common-language installations have been made by large companies to link the data processing activities of geographically scattered offices, warehouses, and plants. For example, a typist at a branch office types an order and the typewriter produces a tape containing the order data, which are then transmitted by Teletype to a central warehouse; here another Teletype prints out the data received in the form of an order, which is used to pick, assemble, and ship the items ordered. But common-language units have brought the benefits of clerical mechanization within the reach of smaller firms. The tape-reading and tape-producing typewriter permits such a firm to prepare many of its records automatically. In writing an invoice, an operator inserts prepunched lengths of tape containing constant customer and product data, causing the typewriter to write those portions of the invoice automatically; the variable data she will type herself on the typewriter keyboard. Calculated data, such as extended cost and selling prices and totals and subtotals, she will transcribe from adding machine tapes prepared by the price clerk. As she completes these operations, the typewriter can produce a tape containing summary data; this tape is later converted to cards for analysis purposes. There are typewriter-computer units available so that calculations can be made automatically and written by the typewriter. Similarly, a book-keeping machine with a tape-producing unit captures data entered and written by the machine. The output of adding and calculating machines can also be captured in punched tape. As noted previously,

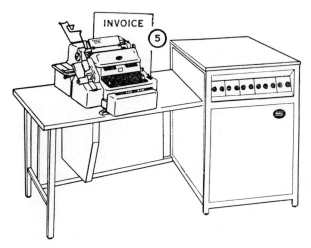

Fig. 4-6. Computyper. (*Friden Corporation.*)

all these machines can now perform the same functions with punched cards.

A number of *communication units* transmit data in punched-tape or punched-card form over a distance by telegraph, telephone, and private line. Teletype is the original such device, and it transmits data in punched-tape form and receives them either in the form of perforated tape or written copy or both simultaneously. Another device transmits data in punched-card form over leased telephone lines and receives them on a standard card-punch unit, which duplicates the card that was transmitted. Several related devices enable punched-card data to be transmitted over an ordinary long-distance circuit, thus saving the expense of leased wire service. All these telephone data communication units permit direct voice communication over the same telephone circuits.

Data communication will grow as the use of automatic data processing methods grows, especially within the confines of individual

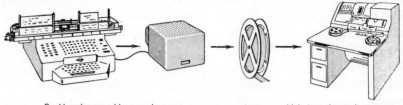

Bookkeeping machine produces . . . . tape. . . which tape-to-card converter

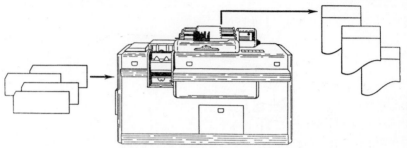

puts in form of punched cards so that data can be processed into desired reports

FIG. 4-7. How punched-paper-tape output of common-language bookkeeping machine is processed into management reports. Frequently, smaller businesses will send tape to a data processing service bureau, which converts it to punched cards to print reports. (*National Cash Register Company.*)

CONSTRUCTION SITE   HOME OFFICE

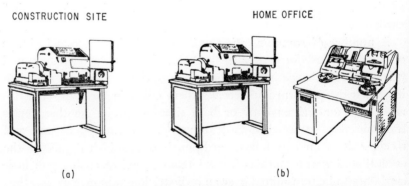

(a)   (b)

FIG. 4-8. (*a*) Construction site. Payroll information is punched into a transmittal tape, which is Teletyped daily to the home office. (*b*) Home office. The information is received at the data processing department both in tape form and in typed report form. The information on the tape is transferred to punched cards by a tape-to-card punch. (*International Business Machines Corporation.*)

firms. Various departments and activities will be directly linked with a central data processing department to reduce the time and work of preparing operating records. For example, it will be possible for a worker in the plant to punch in at a station when he is coming on shift or changing from one operation to another and for all the relevant data to be automatically transmitted to the data processing center. Again, inquiry stations can be set up at various locations, enabling desired data to be automatically transmitted from the data processing center.

Conversion Units

Punched paper tape differs markedly from a punched card in one respect: it is not a unit record. A length of tape can contain various data pertaining to a number of transactions. Although there are tape readers that can locate specific data on a tape, it is not possible to sort and group such data in report form. It is necessary to convert the punched tape to punched cards by using a *tape-to-card converter*. This unit reads the punched tape and automatically punches cards with all or part of the data in the tape. The cards are then processed by standard units.

There are other types of conversion units available:

A *card-to-tape* converter reads punched cards and reproduces the data automatically in punched-paper-tape form; this is often done when data are to be transmitted by Teletype.

A *tag-to-card* converter translates data appearing in small price tags or tickets (such as those used on garments in stores) to standard punched cards for the preparation of inventory and other analyses.

A *card-to-card* converter punches 80-column IBM cards from 90-column Remington Rand cards.

A *paper tape-to-magnetic tape* converter eliminates the necessity of first converting paper tape to punched-card form before the data can appear in magnetic-tape form for input to an electronic computer (see below).

Computers

In the early 1950s, a new class of data processing equipment made its bow to business: electronic computers. An outgrowth of wartime devices used in military and scientific work, computers have the distinction of being possibly the only type of office equipment ever to fire the popular imagination. Their astonishing speed in manipulating and computing prodigious quantities of data soon earned them a Sunday-supplement reputation as "giant brains." Even though experts stubbornly insist that computers are, in most respects, little better than faithful morons, each manufacturer's announcement of a bigger, newer, better model still starts a new round of metaphoric excess.

The term *electronic computer* can embrace a number of devices ranging from a small unit coupled to a bookkeeping machine to the huge LARC and STRETCH systems manufactured by Remington Rand and IBM. The computers discussed in this section resemble the latter systems and are more correctly termed *electronic data processing machines*. This means that they not only possess computational ability but also perform a number of other data processing operations, such as storing data, comparing items, and printing records. These machines are distinguished, also, by their "logical" ability imparted by a stored program.

A full explanation of computers is not intended here. The reader interested in more detailed discussion of these complex systems can refer to three recent books on the subject,[1] and also to an IBM manual entitled "Introduction to IBM Data Processing Systems." The subject of computers is introduced mainly to acquaint management with a type of equipment becoming more widely used in business data processing. The rapid progress being made by the several manufacturers in the field makes the use of such systems by even small firms a distinct possibility in the near future.

But it must be pointed out that, even if compact and inexpensive electronic data processing systems were to make punched-card systems outmoded tomorrow, they would not eliminate the basic principles underlying the planning, installation, and use of punched-card data processing. These principles are identical with those underlying the application of electronic data processing methods. The time and work spent applying punched-card methods is not lost, consequently, but

---

[1] William D. Bell, *A Management Guide to Electronic Computers,* McGraw-Hill Book Company, Inc., New York, 1957; George Kozmetsky and Paul Kircher, *Electronic Computers and Management Control.* McGraw-Hill Book Company, Inc., New York, 1956; John A. Postley, *Computers and People,* McGraw-Hill Book Company, Inc., New York, 1960.

only brings a firm closer to the effective use of any automatic system that may take over in the near or distant future.

How Computers Work. Computers were originally called electronic because their electric circuits were designed around the use of vacuum tubes. The newer circuits using transistors are still electronic, since these solid-state devices perform the same function as vacuum tubes. When data, coded in the form of electric impulses, flow through an electronic circuit, the pattern of the impulses causes the tubes or transistors to switch the flow to other circuits, to count certain impulses passing through, or otherwise to direct the current in accordance with a

FIG. 4-9. Burroughs Corporation's B200 series of electronic computers have been designed specifically to speed up the processing of punched card data. The unit illustrated is the B270 which will accept documents encoded with magnetic ink as well as punched cards. The components shown are two multiple tape listers (for listing data on checks), magnetic tape unit (optional, for faster processing time), sorter-reader (for reading and sorting magnetically encoded documents), central processor, and card reader.

predetermined program. Early computers used electromagnetic telephone relays, but their speed and capacity was limited by the functioning of the relays. The substitution of tubes, and now transistors, enables computers to handle data literally with the speed of light.

In their internal operation computers use a number system which takes advantage of the one-or-off state of a tube or transistor. It is called the binary number system and uses the base or root of 2 (in contrast to the decimal system, which uses a root of 10), so that quantities can be represented as groups of ones and zeroes. Thus 1 will indicate the presence of a signal in a tube or transistor (on) and 0 the absence of a signal (off). Data in decimal form can, however, be received as input by the computer, converted automatically to binary form for internal manipulation, and emitted as output again in decimal form. Data in the form of alphabetic characters or special symbols can be handled in the same way.

A computer carries out a given procedure under the direction of a *stored program*. The program consists of detailed step-by-step instructions stored within the machine, telling it what to do with various data under various conditions. Computers cannot do what they have not first been told to do. A program written for a computer must, therefore, anticipate every alternative which might arise during a particular procedure.

Generally, there are five main components of a computer:

1. Input unit
2. Memory unit
3. Arithmetic unit
4. Control console
5. Output unit

The *input unit* is a device able to read recorded data and introduce it into the computer. The data may be recorded in punched cards, punched paper tape, or magnetic tape. The unit used to take data from punched cards would be a card reader, which senses card holes and translates them into the electric impulses understood by the computer.

The *memory unit* stores data received from the input unit and holds it until it is needed for processing. Depending on the computer's design, a memory unit stores also the computer's program, the intermediate results of computation and processing, various constant data (i.e., rate tables) used in processing, and final answers to be read out to the computer's output unit. There are several types of memory units: magnetic drum, magnetic core plane, magnetic tape, and magnetic disks. Each type has individual advantages, depending on the computer's application.

The *arithmetic unit* of the computer adds, subtracts, multiplies, and divides on instructions from the stored program. This unit is also called the *logic unit,* permitting the computer to take an alternative course of action under predetermined conditions. In following the step-by-step instructions of the stored program for a payroll procedure, for example, the arithmetic unit will test for the amount of year-to-date earnings of an employee. If the amount is below a certain limit, it will compute and deduct the periodic FICA contribution. If the amount exceeds the limit, the unit will skip this deduction and proceed to compute net earnings. This is a very simple illustration of logical ability exercised by the arithmetic unit. Much more involved exception procedures can be programmed for the modern computer.

The *control console* gives an operator manual supervision over the computer and also the means with which to handle unusual situations. If it is suspected that the computer is emitting erroneous information, the malfunctioning can often be corrected at the console. The console is also the operator's medium of communication with all parts of the computer and the computer's medium of communication with the

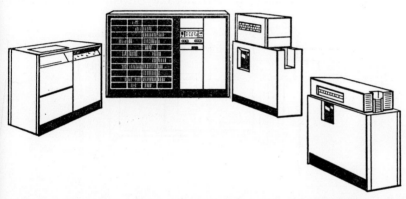

Fig. 4-10. Remington Rand's Univac solid-state computer typifies the smaller, faster systems using transistors instead of vacuum tubes. System above is composed of (from left) high-speed printer, central processor, read-punch unit, and high-speed card reader.

operator. The operator can make an inquiry as to the stock status of an item, for example, and receive the answer in written form from an electric typewriter. Lights flashing on the console can tell the operator that the computer has encountered an error, and he can take steps accordingly. Sometimes the console is used to feed a complex and untested program into the computer.

The *output unit* of a computer can produce punched cards, punched tape, magnetic tape, or printed records. The type of output unit used will depend on how fast results are required. High-speed printers of various kinds are constantly being developed to keep pace with higher and higher processing speeds.

Random Access. Some computer manufacturers have modified their machines to meet the requirements of certain kinds of business. A merchandising business, for example, requires a data processing system capable of storing information relating to perhaps thousands of individual items in inventory. But such a system must give quick— and random—access to any individual stock record so that it can be updated as items are sold or received into inventory. Although efficient inventory control is possible with punched cards or even magnetic tape, some inventories are so huge and variegated that much time would be occupied searching through thousands of cards or reels of tape to locate data on specific items.

Accordingly, some manufacturers have augmented the memory capacity of their machines to store not only inventory but customer

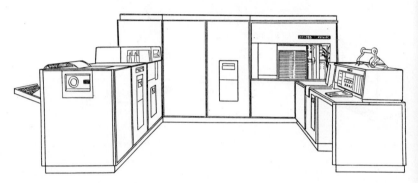

Fig. 4-11. IBM's 305 Ramac data processing machine was among first of the random-access units, permitting data stored in its disk memory to be quickly located and retrieved.

and other data and have also devised means whereby these data can be retrieved and read out quickly, regardless of the sequence in which they may be stored. The result is a computer able to keep a firm's records current practically up to the last transaction.

The Remington Rand Univac File-Computer, for example, has additional magnetic-drum storage capacity for 1,800,000 digits of information, with rapid random access in the form of read-write heads placed above the drums. The Burroughs Corporation's 220 computer can be linked with a Datafile unit providing storage for 550,000,000 digits on a series of 50 magnetic-tape loops rotating under a read-write head.

Random access is especially valuable if it can be performed simultaneously with related routines. For example, if the computer could simultaneously update stored inventory records as it processes order data into a finished invoice, a business could enjoy the benefits of in-line processing. This is the same principle as that governing manual clerical methods. In the conventional office, when an item is withdrawn from inventory for shipment to a customer, clerks make changes in all the ledger accounts affected. They have random access to any account simultaneously as other clerks are completing the order-invoice routine. Thus, in-line processing overcomes some of the disadvantages inherent in batching, referred to earlier.

The IBM Ramac 305 is an example of a computer able to perform in-line processing. The name *Ramac* is a contraction of *random-access method of accounting and control*. The unit possesses some of the abilities of a standard punched-card installation but has, in addition, a *disk memory* storing up to 10 million characters of numerical and alphabetical data on 50 steel disks rotating on a vertical spindle. Access to these data is by means of an access arm with a forked read-write head, which can reach any desired track on the top or bottom of any disk in a matter of milliseconds. For faster access, multiple access arms can be used.

Built around this disk memory are the other data processing components, similar to those found in other computers: magnetic drum for storing the machine's program, output printer, card punch, and control console.

A more detailed description of the Ramac 305's operation is contained in the Case Book. The Remington Rand File-Computer's operation is also described there.

5

How a Punched-card System Works

Because they must necessarily function within a framework long established by custom, law, and accounting practice, manual and punched-card methods of data processing can be compared with one another as they apply to familiar procedures. The comparison will serve to illustrate how a typical punched-card system works. In this chapter, the familiar procedures chosen for this purpose are order processing and invoicing, accounts receivable, purchasing, accounts payable, inventory control, and payroll. Although this dissection of data processing into its parts may seem to violate the integrated, or total-system, approach, it is done to reveal how the application of punched-card methods to each procedure actually improves the chances of integration. As will be seen, punched cards enable the output of one procedure to become automatically the entry to the next procedure—all because the unit-record principle of punched cards holds data available for reuse.

Order Processing and Invoicing

As standard as they are, these procedures vary from company to company. The following order processing and invoicing procedures are, however, fairly common to manufacturing firms receiving orders from customers or salesmen and invoicing after the order has been shipped.

Manual Method. When an order is received in the office from a customer or salesman, it is subjected to a series of manual checks. Sometimes the order is registered, with a clerk recording date, order number, name of customer, items ordered, etc., on a spread sheet. The order goes to the credit department for a check on the customer's credit standing and credit limit; this step is often minimized by scrutinizing only exceptions. The order is next sent to an analysis clerk, who determines what departments will require working copies to enable the order to be filled; in this instance, it is assumed the order calls for items which can be shipped out of finished stock.

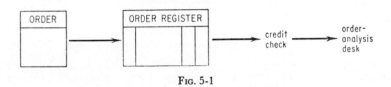

FIG. 5-1

The order is recopied by a typist to a multipart form to provide the required working copies.

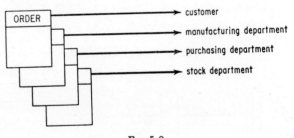

FIG. 5-2

When the order has been filled, a shipping department copy (with quantity and weight shipped, freight charges, and out-of-stock, back-order, and other notations) is returned to the office for pricing. A clerk checks prices against a price book and writes them in. Another clerk extends cost and selling prices, applies discounts, and calculates the net total of the order.

Fig. 5-3

All the data must now be copied once again by a typist preparing the finished invoice. A seven-part form is used to furnish invoice copies to the customer and to the departments directly affected by the order.

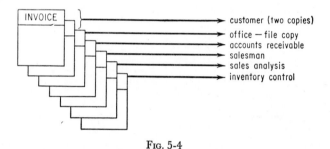

Fig. 5-4

A clerk then prepares an adding machine control tape, totaling the invoice amounts of this and other orders billed during the day. This tape and the accounts receivable copies are sent to the accounting department for posting.

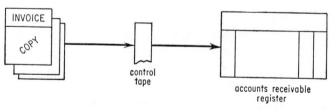

Fig. 5-5

Other invoice copies enable the inventory record to be updated, the production schedule to be made up, and the sales analysis register to be posted.

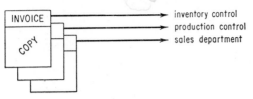

Fɪɢ. 5-6

In the above manual procedure, constant and variable data must be copied several times before the finished invoice can be mailed. Further copying is entailed in posting data from the invoice copies to the various ledgers and records. To reduce this copying, many firms use a combined order-invoice form at the time working copies are typed.

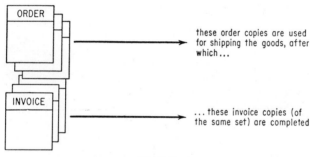

Fɪɢ. 5-7

And, of course, bookkeeping machines will help solve the problem of posting to ledgers. Nevertheless, none of these improvements entirely bridges the gaps between the various stages of processing. Manual recording of constant and variable data is still required at each stage, thereby breeding errors and slowing clerical routine.

Punched-card Method. In punched-card data processing, constant and variable data are copied only once—when they are recorded in punched-card form. Any further recording is performed automatically by the machines.

Order processing and invoicing can be handled in several ways on punched cards. In the following method, the processing steps are roughly in the same sequence as in the manual method above. The reader should remember that a batch of orders is being processed at one time; as explained earlier, similar clerical operations, such as order processing and invoicing, must be grouped to be handled efficiently on punched cards.

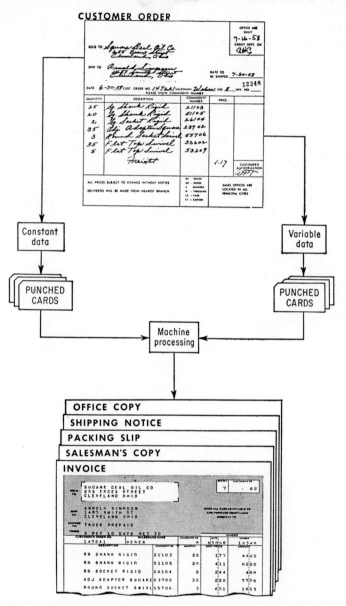

Fig. 5-8. A simplified view of punched-card processing of an invoice from the original order.

A batch of incoming orders would receive their customary checking. Manual registering of the orders may or may not be needed, depending on the degree of control desired.

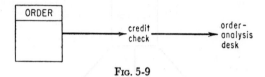

Fig. 5-9

Constant data, in the form of customer and product master cards, are withdrawn from their respective tub files. Other constant data, such as terms of payment, shipping instructions, and salesmen's code numbers, may be prepunched in the customer master cards or punched in their own cards and pulled as part of the customer master card set.

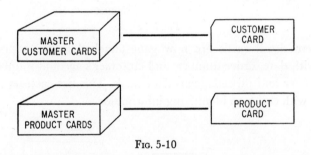

Fig. 5-10

Variable data—particularly quantities of each item ordered by each customer—are punched into duplicated product master cards. The original master cards are returned to the tub file. The duplicated masters are now called *item detail cards*.

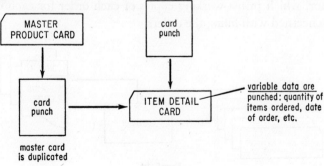

Fig. 5-11

Other variable data—customers' order numbers, date of orders, invoice numbers, etc.—are manually punched into miscellaneous data cards.

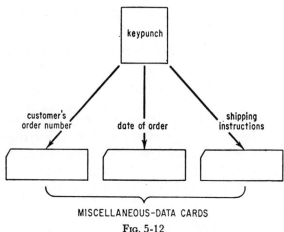

MISCELLANEOUS-DATA CARDS
FIG. 5-12

All item detail cards are now gang-punched by the reproducing punch with date, order number, and customer's account number from the customer and miscellaneous data cards. This ties each set of cards together with common identifying information.

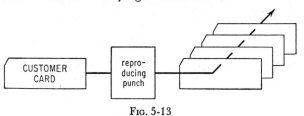

FIG. 5-13

The sets of cards are now run through the accounting machine or tabulator, which prints working copies of each order for each department concerned with filling the orders.

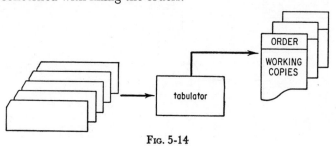

FIG. 5-14

Shipping copies are returned to the office from the warehouse department; for each order, they carry notations enabling card-punch operators to punch quantities shipped, freight charges, taxes, miscellaneous charges, etc., into the appropriate cards. The entire set of cards is now run through the calculating punch, which extends the cost and selling prices on the item detail cards. This machine will also punch a *trailer card,* containing the total tax applying to the order.

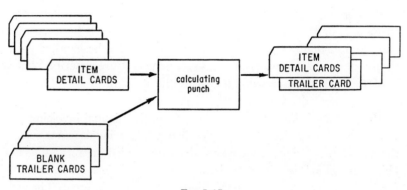

Fig. 5-15

The cards are run through the tabulator, which prints the completed invoices. At the same time, a reproducing punch connected to the tabulator punches an accounts receivable card containing data summarizing each invoice.

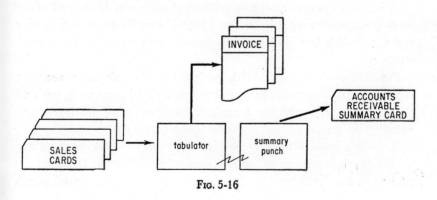

Fig. 5-16

Accounts Receivable

Whether accounts receivable are handled manually or by punched-card data processing, procedure follows a fairly standard pattern: posting of receivables data to ledger accounts, recording remittance data, following up on each account and on collections and delinquencies, and analyzing account activity.

Depending on the kind and size of the business, there are many ways of creating accounts receivable. They may be created through credit applications from customers, through contract agreement with customers, or through written or verbal arrangements between company and customers. Also, accounts receivable can be handled on an open-item or balance-forward basis. The procedure described below is of the balance-forward kind, with the accounts receivable being created as a result of customers' orders.

Manual Method. Continuing along from the manual invoicing procedure previously described, copies of customer invoices are sent to the accounting department, where they are totaled on an adding machine tape. Each invoice total is then posted to ledger cards, one card for each customer, and a new balance is carried forward. The total postings are checked with the adding machine total.

As a further check on accuracy, summary data from each invoice (customer's name, date of invoice, invoice amount, etc.) are posted to an invoice register. This register is totaled, and the total is checked with the original adding machine tape. As payments are received from customers against these accounts, further posting and calculating is necessary to keep each account current. Periodically, the receivables data must be analyzed to furnish the credit and sales departments with information on overdue or delinquent accounts. At the end of the month, statements are prepared and issued to each customer, requiring typists to pull ledger cards and transcribe amounts outstanding to each statement.

Punched-card Method. With punched cards, this same accounts receivable procedure can be handled quickly and accurately, with all the requisite controls for accuracy, thus reducing management's anxiety over customers' indebtedness to the company.

Referring back to the punched-card method of invoicing explained in the previous section, it will be remembered that, at the time the tabulator was printing invoices, a reproducing or summary punch

attached to the tabulator was producing an accounts receivable card
for each invoice.

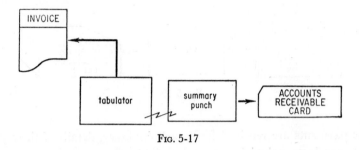

Fig. 5-17

This card contains all the relevant information summarized from
the invoice sufficient to maintain an account receivable for each
customer:

Customer account number	Entry date
Location	Entry code
Trade class	Invoice date
Branch	Invoice number
Salesman number	Discount allowed
	Invoice amount

Punched with these data, the accounts receivable cards can then be
run through the tabulator to produce an invoice register. The machine's total can be checked against an adding machine tape covering
the same invoices.

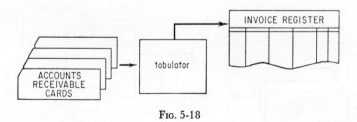

Fig. 5-18

Or the accounts receivable cards can be merged with the daily
sales cards (from the invoicing cycle) to run off a daily sales register
or journal. This report will show if the two sets of cards are in balance
with one another.

The summary cards can then be filed alphabetically (by customer account number) to form an accounts receivable ledger.

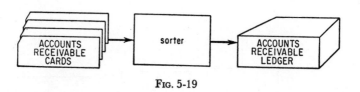

FIG. 5-19

As payments are received from each customer, details of these payments are keypunched into payment cards. Data on returned goods, allowances, and discounts can be similarly punched.

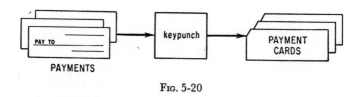

FIG. 5-20

Groups of payment cards can then be run through the tabulator to produce such reports as cash receipts reports and credit and allowance reports.

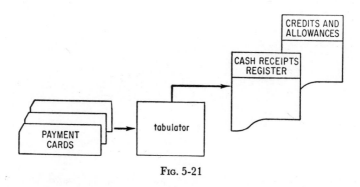

FIG. 5-21

After they have been used to produce these reports, the payment cards are merged with the accounts receivable cards in the ledger file.

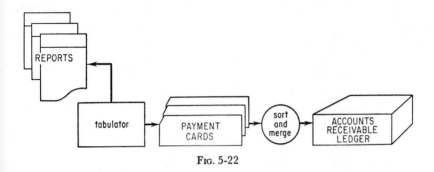

FIG. 5-22

At the end of the accounting period, the accounts receivable and payment cards are merged with customer name-and-address cards and run through the tabulator to produce monthly statements. The tabulator automatically deducts payments made by each customer from the amount outstanding and prints the balance in the statement.

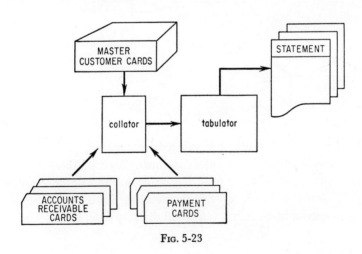

FIG. 5-23

Purchasing

The purchasing procedure consists in receiving written requisitions from departments for various supplies, materials, and equipment. These requisitions are checked by the purchasing department, which makes out purchase orders. Original copies of the purchase orders are sent to vendors, acknowledgement copies to the departments concerned, and a checking copy to the receiving department in readiness for the arrival of the shipment.

Punched-card Method. The names and addresses of vendors are prepunched in master vendor cards. Various items that are regularly purchased by the firm are punched into master item cards. When requisitions are received from departments and checked, variable data such as quantities required and shipping instructions are punched into duplicated item cards and into miscellaneous data cards. These cards, together with the master vendor cards, are then run through the tabulator to print multipart purchase orders.

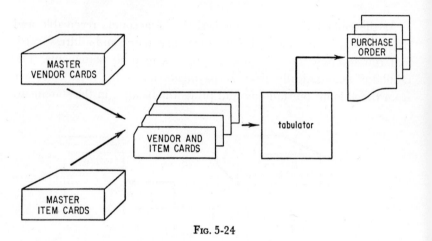

Fig. 5-24

As the purchase orders are printed, a summary punch connected to the tabulator produces *on-order cards*. Each of these cards summarizes the relevant data appearing on each purchase order: description of items ordered, quantities, vendors from whom items are ordered, special instructions, requested delivery date, etc.

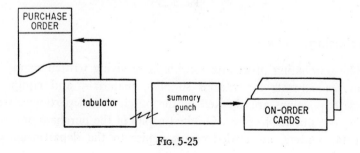

Fig. 5-25

These cards are then grouped in an open-order file.

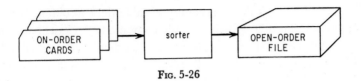

FIG. 5-26

When a vendor has shipped the items requested and they have been received and checked against the receiving copy of the purchase order, receipt cards are punched for each item in the order.

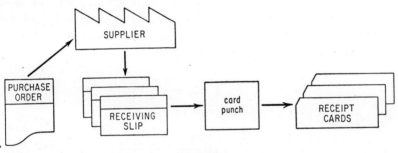

FIG. 5-27

The receipt cards are matched against those in the open-order file, and the set is run through the tabulator to print a receiving report.

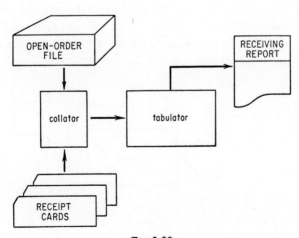

FIG. 5-28

Accounts Payable

The need to break down accounts payable data to obtain accurate cost analysis places a growing burden on manual clerical methods. With punched-card data processing, on the other hand, payables data are immediately available for distribution to the various accounts incurring the liabilities.

Punched-card Method. Following on from the purchasing procedure outlined above, the purchasing department will check each vendor's invoice covering the items ordered and received. These invoices are sent to the machine accounting department where *disbursement* and *distribution cards* are keypunched. The disbursement card will show the total amount owed to a vendor; the distribution card (one for each item listed on the invoice) will show the department charged with the cost of a particular item.

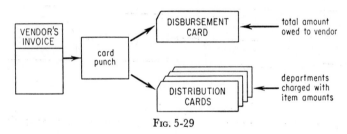

Fig. 5-29

The disbursement and distribution cards are run through the tabulator to print an invoice register. This register gives the accounting department a detailed tally of the various invoices received from vendors and representing payables. It shows, also, the charges allocated to the various departments.

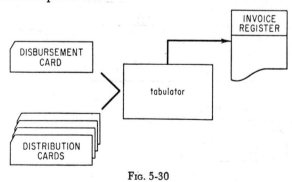

Fig. 5-30

The disbursement cards are filed by due date in an accounts payable file. This file becomes, in fact, the accounts payable ledger. Payables falling due on particular dates can be selected from the file automatically by a sorter.

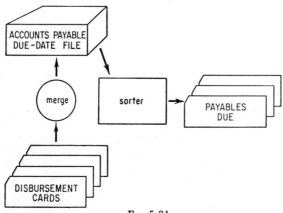

FIG. 5-31

The punched cards representing accounts payable on a specific date are now run through the tabulator to produce a cash disbursements register.

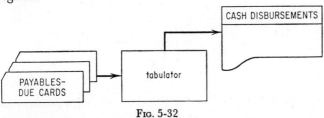

FIG. 5-32

Through the various controls it has set up, the accounting department can check this register for accuracy. Any changes are punched in new cards, and the whole deck is run through the tabulator, which prints checks and vouchers.

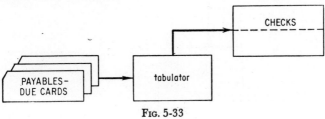

FIG. 5-33

The distribution cards have been filed in a payables distribution file by account number (the number assigned in the firm's chart of accounts).

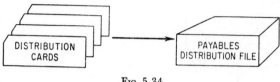

Fig. 5-34

At the end of each accounting period, the distribution cards are run through the tabulator to produce the accounts distribution report. The same cards can be separated into categories of purchasing expenses; summaries can then be prepared for each group of expenditures.

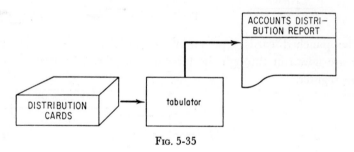

Fig. 5-35

While the distribution report is being printed, summary cards are punched containing the total charge made to each account number. These cards can then become the entry to the general ledger.

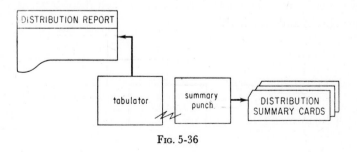

Fig. 5-36

Inventory Control

Whether it consists of raw materials and parts or finished goods (in the case of a manufacturing company) or of merchandise for resale (in the case of a merchandising firm), inventory levels are affected by these main factors:

1. Issues from stock
2. Items on back order
3. Goods returned by customer for credit
4. Purchases returned to suppliers for credit
5. Items currently on order
6. Receipts into stock

Punched-card Method. The above variables can be kept current and related to the over-all inventory picture when handled on punched cards. For instance, from the description of the purchasing procedure, it will be recalled that *on-order* data are in punched-card form. Also, during the accounts payable procedure, cards can be keypunched representing *purchases returned.* Again, during the order processing–invoicing cycle, sales cards were created showing *issues from stock.* Data on *back-order* items can also be in card form. *Receipts into stock* were punched into cards during the purchasing procedure. Data relating to *goods returned by customer* for credit were punched in cards from credit memos during the order processing–invoicing cycle.

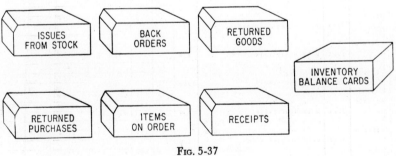

FIG. 5-37

All these cards together contain the data relating to the movement into and out of stock of each item. Finally, held in a file from a previous inventory report period, are *balance cards,* showing stock status of each item on a particular date.

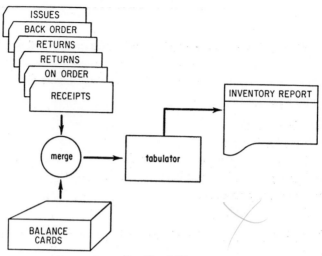

FIG. 5-38

These cards, merged with the balance cards, item for item, are run
through the tabulator to obtain an inventory activity report.

PRODUCT CODE	VENDOR CODE	PACKED	PRODUCT DESCRIPTION	DATE	SIZE	OLD BALANCE	SHIPMENTS RECEIVED	MIN. RETURNS	MAX. SALES	ON HAND	# OF ITEMS OUT	ORDERED
		3093	M 100 CYTELLIN SUSPENSION		1M			144	288			
82338 5				JAN 29 195		139	72		66	145		
		3093		2 12 5		145	60		34	171●		24
			M 14 EPHEDROL W/CODE,NE		1M			36	72			
82341 0				JAN 29 195		37	48		29	56		
		3093	12	2 12 5		56	12		14	54●		12
			GLYCERITES 3 BOROGLYCERIN		1M			1	2			
82350 0				JAN 29 195		3			3			
		3093	12	2 12 5			3		2	1●		2
			GLYCERITES 10 MERTHIOLATE		1M			1	2			
82352 0				JAN 29 195		4			1	3		
		3093	12	2 12 5		3				.3●		
			M 17 HOMICEBRIN		60●			36	72			
82354 0				JAN 29 195		62			2	60		
		3093	72	2 12 5		60			2	58●		
			M 17 HOMICEBRIN		120●			1008	2016			
82355 0				JAN 29 195		1035	531		612	954		
		3093	48	2 12 5		954	725		387	1292●		288
			M 17 HOMICEBRIN		1M			720	1440			
82356 0				JAN 29 195		708	543		476	775		
		3093	12	2 12 5		775	434		399	810●		288
			M-240 ILETIN U 40		10●			1500	3000			
82357 0				JAN 29 195		1779	500		538	1741		
		3093	500	2 12 5		1741	501		452	1790●		500
			M-280 ILETIN U 80		10●			500	1000			
82358 0				JAN 29 195		615	201		172	644		
			500	2 12 5		644	204		136	712●		100

BERGEN DRUG CO.   PERPETUAL INVENTORY

FIG. 5-39

This report will show, for a given period, the complete movement into and out of stock of each item.

As this report is printed, a summary punch prepares summary cards showing activity and status over the chosen inventory period. They will also show the final stock balance of each item. These cards become the balance cards for the next inventory period.

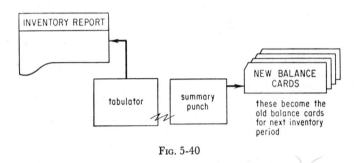

FIG. 5-40

Payroll

Payroll is often one of the first procedures to be converted to punched-card methods. The advantages being sought by management in making the conversion are chiefly (1) a faster, less costly method of handling the numerous details of payroll preparation and (2) greater ease in obtaining accurate, prompt distribution of labor costs to the various accounts. Even with a straight hourly payroll, cost analysis is laborious and time-consuming when manual methods are used. When piecework, incentives, and other complications are introduced into the procedure, many kinds of cost analysis become virtually impossible.

The numerous steps involved in making up a payroll by manual means are listed on page 80.

Punched-card Method. As many as possible of the constant data used in payroll preparation are prepunched and kept in tub files. Thus, the transcribing of variable data is kept to a minimum. There are master cards for employee's name, regular deductions, and tax deduction status. The master name card contains name, clock number, Social Security number, and rate at which employee is paid hourly. The constant deduction card contains the employee's number, description of the deduction, and the amount per pay period. The tax deduc-

MANUAL METHOD OF HANDLING PAYROLL

1 read time card; post hours to work sheet

2 look up rate; post rate to work sheet

3 multiply hours by rate; record product on work sheet

4 post product to gross-pay detail column

5 add numbers in gross-pay detail column; record total on work sheet

6 look up exemptions for individual employee on employee history card

7 look up tax in tax table (or compute) corresponding to gross pay and exemptions

8 post tax to work sheet

9 compute FOAB deduction. post to work sheet as trial FOAB deduction

10 look up total FOAB withholdings to date on employee history card. post to work sheet

11 add trial deduction. post total to work sheet

12 look up standard FOAB total in tax table

13 compare total from step 11 with standard amount

14 if standard amount is larger, post trial amount to work sheet in deduction column as FOAB deduction

    if standard amount is smaller, subtract from total obtained in step 11 and post difference to work sheet. subtract difference from trial deduction; post result to work sheet in deduction column as FOAB deduction

15 look up remaining deductions in employee history file. post to work sheet

16 add all deductions. post total to work sheet

17 subtract total deductions from gross pay. enter difference on work sheet as net pay

Fig. 5-41. The various steps needed in the manual method of making up a payroll.

tion card contains the employee's number, and predetermined withholding tax amount for his exemption class.

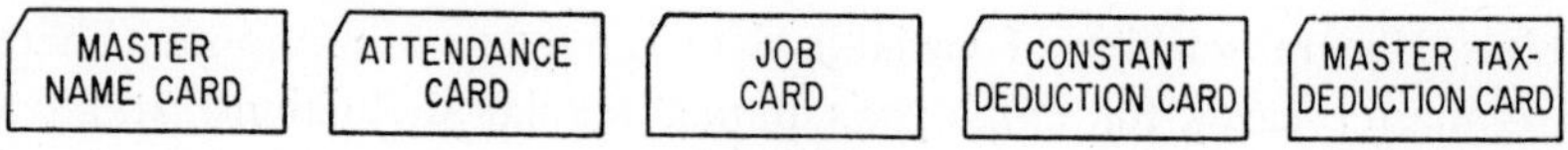

| MASTER NAME CARD | ATTENDANCE CARD | JOB CARD | CONSTANT DEDUCTION CARD | MASTER TAX-DEDUCTION CARD |

Fig. 5-42

Each day data from the master cards are reproduced in daily *attendance* (or *clock*) *cards,* which are the employees' records of times worked. At the end of the day, these attendance cards are merged with *job cards,* which are prepunched for each operation involved in the manufacture of a particular item. The cards are run through a calculating punch, which punches into the job cards data on each employee's output and his earnings for that job. The same data are punched into prepunched cards for other jobs. Also calculated are the attendance cards, showing each employee's total earnings for the working day. Thus the job cards distribute the cost of employees' labor to particular operations, and the attendance cards show total daily earnings of each employee.

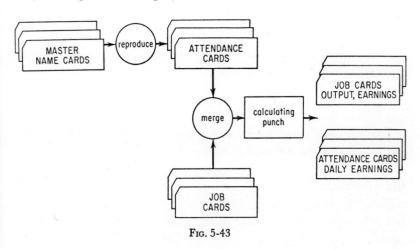

FIG. 5-43

The job cards are separated from the attendance cards and filed in a *labor-distribution file.* The cards in this file will later be used for cost analysis purposes. The attendance cards are filed in a *daily earnings file.*

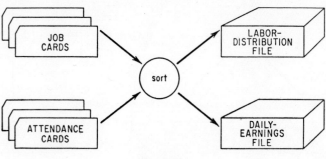

FIG. 5-44

For a given pay period, say, a week, blank cards are merged with daily earnings cards and run through the calculating punch to create a weekly earnings card. The daily earnings cards are returned to the daily attendance file.

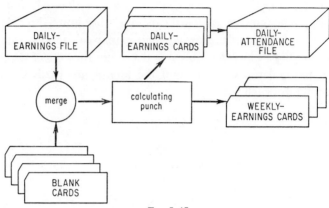

FIG. 5-45

The weekly-earnings cards are merged with *year-to-date earnings cards* and with the constant deduction cards and tax deduction cards. When run through the calculating punch, the weekly earnings cards and year-to-date cards are punched with net weekly earnings; the calculating punch calculates the total deductions for each employee and subtracts them from the gross pay shown on the weekly earnings cards.

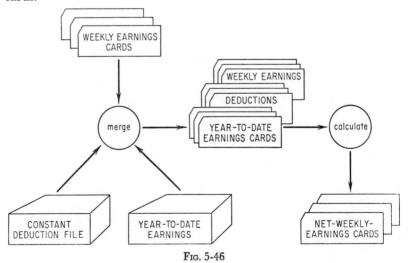

FIG. 5-46

The cards are now run through the tabulator, which prints the payroll register. This record shows all the earnings and deduction details for each employee for the pay period.

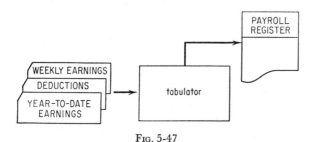

Fɪɢ. 5-47

When the payroll register has been checked and corrections made in the relevant cards, the cards are run through the tabulator to print pay checks and vouchers for each employee. At the same time, the summary punch produces new year-to-date earnings cards reflecting the latest pay period. The latter cards become the year-to-date earnings cards for the next pay period.

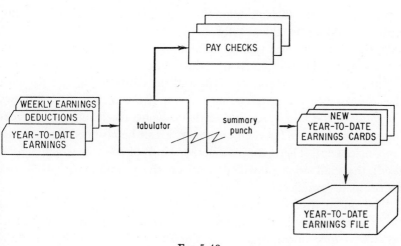

Fɪɢ. 5-48

Much more complex payroll procedures can be processed on punched cards. In the Case Book, the payroll procedure of Marquette Division, Curtiss-Wright Corporation, is described.

Accounting Controls

When an entire procedure is converted to punched-card methods, one may well wonder what safeguards are available against error and fraud. The answer is that certain controls are set up within and alongside the punched-card system to assure that all data that should be processed have, in fact, been processed. One of these controls is *document control*, which is a means of making sure that source documents (such as customer orders) are not lost or mislaid. Under manual methods, such controls are common; for example, registering orders as they are received, assigning order numbers, and using transmittal slips and routing slips. These controls become even more necessary under automatic data processing, since errors in recording original data can be very quickly perpetuated throughout a given procedure.

To check the results of processing, accounting controls must be included in a procedure. These can take the form of arithmetical checks that compare the total arrived at by punched-card methods with a total made manually. An accounting control can also consist in comparing two totals arrived at within the system but derived from two different sets of cards. For example, a common type of accounting control is to check the tabulator's total accumulated during invoicing with an adding machine total made separately of the individual ledger entries. Another type of accounting control is *zero balancing*. For example, the sales cards used in billing can be merged with the accounts receivable summary cards and the entire group run through the tabulator to produce a sales register. If the register listing shows the totals of the sales cards and of the accounts receivable cards agreeing with each other for each customer, it can be assumed that no discrepancies exist. There are many other kinds of controls which can be used; the kind adopted will depend on the procedure involved and on company practice.

The question of *audit trails* arises when a punched-card system is being contemplated. In conventional accounting practice, copies of essential source documents are retained to enable an auditor to validate the company's financial records. Further, the control over a particular transaction is usually divided among several persons, resulting usually in effective accounting control. When procedures are handled on punched cards or by an electronic data processing system, however, many of the basic documents forming the audit trail take the form of cards or magnetic tape or are no longer needed. More-over, control over transactions tends to pass into fewer hands with a centralized data processing department.

Auditing practice has adapted itself to these changes taking place in record keeping. Accountants are generally satisfied if stringent controls are maintained over the entry of data into an automatic data

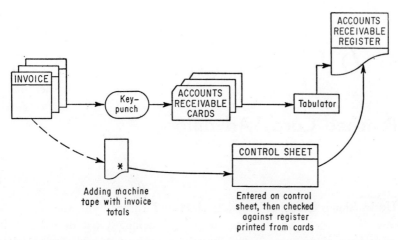

FIG. 5-49. A portion of a flow chart, showing provision that has been made for accounting control.

processing system and if cards and tapes containing essential financial data are filed. Richard T. Baker, a general partner of the accounting firm Ernst & Ernst Company, has observed: "There will be little reason to consider electronic data processing as having a weakening effect upon internal control and the work of the certified public accountant, providing, of course, that there is proper supervision, planning, procedures, and control."[1]

It is always advisable for a company to consult its auditors when planning a punched-card installation to make sure that the necessary controls and audit trails are included in the new procedures.

[1] *Data Processing:* Proceedings of Annual Conference of National Machine Accounts Association, 1959.

6

Punched Cards' Advantage: Analysis

Under the pressure of growing costs and competition, management must have some way of measuring the company's performance. It must have some way of analyzing the records of the company so that they have significance in gauging the company's operating efficiency, its market position, and its profit. Without such analysis, the firm's records have only archival interest. So that management can have decision-making data with which to guide the current and future course of the business, certain critical data must be extracted from the records and put in the form of action reports. Records prepared manually frustrate attempts to isolate and rearrange facts having a real bearing on management's objectives. Punched-card data processing, on the other hand, has the advantage of keeping data always "above the surface," ready for quick, accurate analysis. Picking up from the preceding chapter, this chapter shows how the punched-card method makes analysis a natural by-product for each procedure.

Sales Analysis

Manual Method. The only way in which pertinent data can be isolated and summarized by manual methods is by further manual copy-

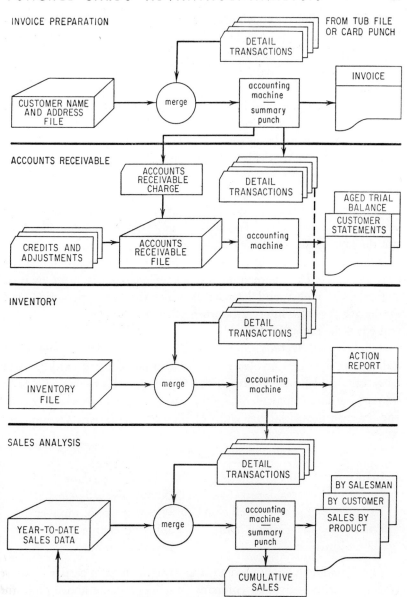

INVOICE PREPARATION

DETAIL TRANSACTIONS

FROM TUB FILE OR CARD PUNCH

CUSTOMER NAME AND ADDRESS FILE

merge

accounting machine — summary punch

INVOICE

ACCOUNTS RECEIVABLE

ACCOUNTS RECEIVABLE CHARGE

DETAIL TRANSACTIONS

AGED TRIAL BALANCE

CUSTOMER STATEMENTS

CREDITS AND ADJUSTMENTS

ACCOUNTS RECEIVABLE FILE

accounting machine

INVENTORY

DETAIL TRANSACTIONS

INVENTORY FILE

merge

accounting machine

ACTION REPORT

SALES ANALYSIS

DETAIL TRANSACTIONS

BY SALESMAN

BY CUSTOMER

SALES BY PRODUCT

YEAR-TO-DATE SALES DATA

merge

accounting machine — summary punch

CUMULATIVE SALES

Fig. 6-1. Flow chart showing how business data interrelate with one another. The output of invoice preparation, for example, becomes the input for accounts receivable, and so on through other procedures. Punched-card methods not only make use of these data relationships but also enable data to be held always available for analysis and processing into management reports. (*International Business Machines Corporation.*)

ing. This unavoidable copying limits severely the variety and comprehensiveness of the analyses. In making up a sales analysis in the conventional office, for example, a clerk would first have to post to a spread sheet relevant data from each invoice copy to show sales by product class.

At the end of the month, the individual dollar amounts for each product class are totaled and then recopied in the preparation of a report summarizing sales by product class.

But this procedure yields only an analysis of sales by product. To obtain other analyses (by salesman, by territory, by size of shipment, by customer, etc), the original data would have to be copied from invoice copies to other spread sheets and so arranged that these other breakdowns were shown. To obtain a more refined analysis, such as one showing gross profit for each product class, would require setting up yet another recopying procedure to filter out and summarize the relevant data. The more analyses management seeks from manual methods, the higher and broader becomes the paper pyramid—and the longer the time interval between when the information is needed and when the report is ready.

Punched-card Method. Sales analysis is a natural by-product when order processing and invoicing are handled on punched cards. It will be remembered from the preceding chapter that this cycle ended with transaction data still available in two sets of cards: (1) the *sales cards,* one for each line of billing, and (2) the *accounts receivable summary cards.*

The sales cards each contain the following data:

Item code number	Customer's account number
Quantity of item shipped	Customer's trade class
Extended cost price of each item	Salesman's code number
Extended selling price of item	Shipping charge
Date of invoice	Invoice number

The kind and variety of data appearing in a sales card will vary, of course, with individual company practice, but the above data are typical and sufficient to illustrate the analyses obtainable from the order processing–invoicing cycle. For example, the sales cards covering a month's transactions can be sorted on item code numbers, merged with matching master product cards, and run through the tabulator to obtain a sales analysis by product. At the same time, a summary punch could produce *year-to-date summary cards* for each item.

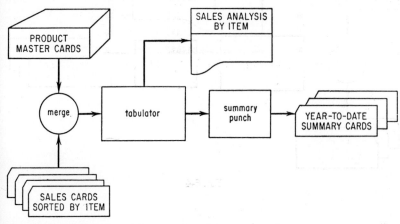

Fɪɢ. 6-2

The sales cards can be sorted by customer account number and then merged with matching customer master cards (to get the alphabetical name of each customer) to print a sales analysis by customer.

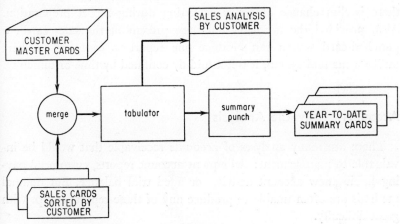

Fɪɢ. 6-3

Similarly, the cards can be used to obtain sales analyses by salesmen, by territory, and by any other factor that management thinks is significant to its purposes.

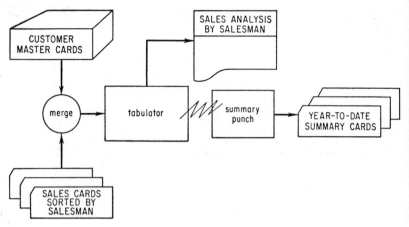

Fɪɢ. 6-4

Even more comprehensive reports are possible when the sales cards are merged with prepunched cards containing sales quota or budget information or previous year-to-date figures.

It should be noted that *all the data entering the analysis cycle have been verified for accuracy* in the previous order processing–invoicing cycle. Provided common-sense accounting controls are maintained, there is slim chance of errors occurring during report preparation. Also, provided the necessary data are present in the sales cards, a punched-card system can produce one report as easily as another; unlike a manual system, it is not unduly confined by time or difficulty.

Accounts Receivable Analysis

There are many analyses of accounts receivable that would be invaluable to management: delinquent account reports, customers' paying habits, new account activity, or aged trial balance. But manual methods are often unable to produce any of these reports except with great difficulty.

Punched-card Method. The preparation of a monthly aged trial balance provides a good example of how punched-card data processing yields an essential analysis as a by-product of a routine procedure, e.g., order processing and invoicing. In the foregoing chapter, it was described how accounts receivable summary cards punched as invoices were printed and merged with payment and master customer cards to produce month-end statements.

These same cards can be run through the tabulator to print the aged trial balance. It is possible to handle the cards in such a way that receivables data will automatically appear on the aged trial balance according to the length of time such amounts have been owed by customers. Thus, receivables for any given customer account number can be listed with the current items separated from the aged items.

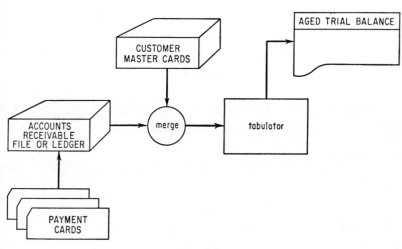

Fɪɢ. 6-5

Purchasing Analysis

The records prepared during the purchase order–receiving cycle contain data which are reused for (1) accounts payable, (2) inventory control, and (3) purchasing department management. Many of these data are also needed for production control purposes. If the processing of purchasing and receiving data is handled manually, the extent to which these data can be reused is limited.

Punched-card Method. The purchasing department itself can derive several report advantages from punched-card processing of purchasing and receiving data. From Chapter 4, it will be remembered that on-order cards were created as a by-product of purchase order writing.

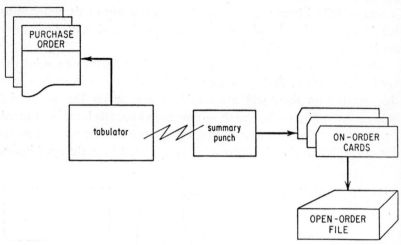

FIG. 6-6

Held in an open-order file, these cards are continually revised by receipts of merchandise and by the issuing of new purchase orders. Thus, at any one time, they represent all the items on which the firm is awaiting delivery. They can be used to print an on-order status report.

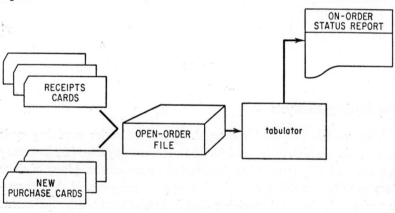

FIG. 6-7

From the item description cards used in printing the purchase orders, a parts catalogue can be prepared, which lists nomenclature, part number, finish, size, etc., for the use of various production departments.

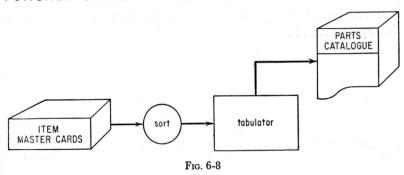

FIG. 6-8

Depending on the company's individual requirements, many other analyses are available as a result of converting purchase order writing to punched cards. Two examples are an analysis of purchases by vendors and a report showing seasonal purchasing patterns.

Accounts Payable Analysis

Manual methods restrict the variety of analyses which should be periodically made of payables data. Management cannot function effectively if the data processing system is depriving it of reliable and timely cost information.

Punched-card Method. As a result of the accounts payable procedure described in the previous chapter, two sets of cards exist in two files:

• *Distribution cards:* One card was punched for each line item on each vendor's invoice and shows the account that is charged with the expenditure. These cards are filed in the *distribution payables file*.

• *Disbursement cards:* One card was punched for each vendor's invoice amount. These cards were used to print the cash disbursements record and also the checks and vouchers sent to the vendors. They are now filed in the *paid file*.

In these two files, then, are punched cards showing (1) the company's disbursements to particular vendors and (2) how these expenditures have been distributed to various accounts within the company. Moreover, the accuracy of the data in these cards has been proved; the cards need merely be sorted on the desired factor. For example, when sorted on account number sequence, the distribution cards can be run through the tabulator to provide an expense distribution by department.

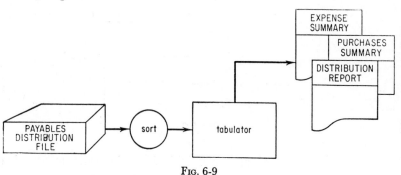

Fig. 6-9

The disbursement cards in the paid file can be sorted by vendor to obtain a report analyzing purchases by vendor.

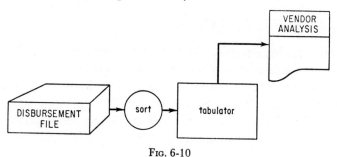

Fig. 6-10

While this report is printed, summary cards can be punched for use in preparing a report showing the total volume each vendor has sold to the firm over a period.

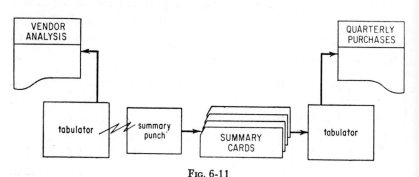

Fig. 6-11

If other accounts payable cards are punched from vouchers recording disbursements other than those covered by vendor invoices, these can also be used to prepare reports.

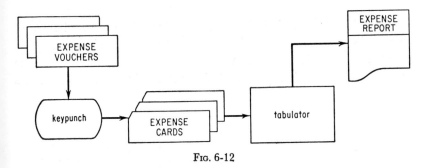

FIG. 6-12

Inventory Analysis

The need for periodic analyses has become particularly pressing in the case of inventory. With both manufacturing and merchandising firms, the costs of maintaining stocks of raw materials, finished goods, or merchandise for resale have increased over the past few years. For example, from a report showing inventory turnover, a merchandising firm can determine the adequacy of stock levels. A low turnover figure will indicate excessive inventory in relation to sales; an unusually high turnover figure may indicate too costly, too frequent buying from suppliers. Because of the mass of data involved, an accurate turnover report is usually beyond the capability of manual clerical methods.

Punched-card Method. Referring back to the inventory control procedure explained in Chapter 4, it will be recalled that *new balance cards* were created at the end of the inventory control cycle. These cards contain all the data necessary to produce, for example, turnover reports for any or all items.

At the end of each month, the balance cards for those items on which turnover information is desired are reproduced and held in a file until the time the turnover report is needed. They are then sorted by item code number groups and processed by the calculating punch. The punch (1) totals the month-end balances in each card and (2) divides this total by the number of months covered by the report to obtain the average monthly inventory of each item.

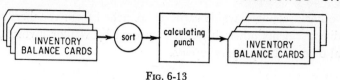

Fig. 6-13

Over this same period, *issues to date* have been carried forward in each balance card. The calculating punch divides this figure by the average monthly inventory to obtain the turnover for the period. The cards are then run through the tabulator to obtain the turnover report.

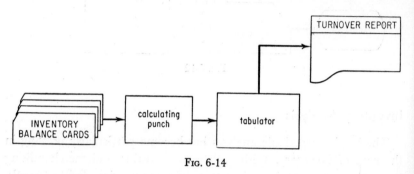

Fig. 6-14

The balance cards can also be used to prepare reports showing velocity of movement of merchandise, branch inventory levels, inventory by class of merchandise, etc.

Payroll Analysis

The distribution of payroll expense is essential to cost accounting. Manual clerical methods are sufficiently hard put processing the average payroll without taking on the task of preparing reports showing in detail how payroll costs are apportioned. Punched-card data processing makes these reports a routine by-product of the payroll procedure.

Punched-card Method. The payroll procedure described in the foregoing chapter mentioned job cards held in a labor-distribution file. These cards were punched to show what part of each employee's earnings and hours were charged to specific operations. These cards can be sorted by department, merged with employee name cards, and run through the tabulator to obtain a labor-distribution register showing the distribution of each employee's time and earnings.

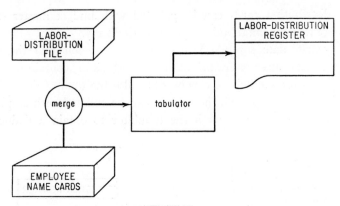

Fig. 6-15

These cards can also be sorted by job number to obtain a parts-cost analysis.

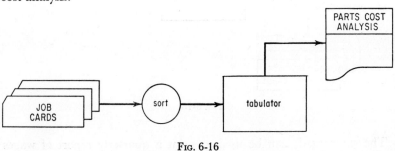

Fig. 6-16

If they have been prepunched with standard hour data, the cards can be run through a calculating punch, which calculates and punches an efficiency ratio (i.e., 108 per cent of standard, 89 per cent of standard). They are then sorted by department number and run through the tabulating machine, which prints a production efficiency report totaled for each department.

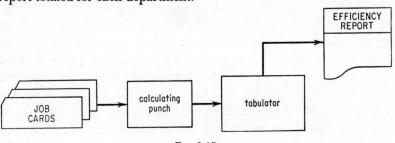

Fig. 6-17

The distribution cards can be collated with budget master cards to prepare departmental budget reports periodically.

The year-to-date summary cards, summary-punched at the time employees' pay checks were printed by the tabulator, contain not only the total of each employee's earnings but also the total of deductions. Thus, for each pay period, these cards can be collated with employee master cards and run through the tabulator to obtain a deduction register.

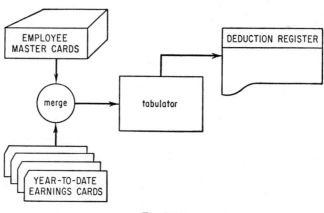

FIG. 6-18

The same cards can be used to print a quarterly report of wages taxable under FICA on the official government forms.

Analysis: The Essential By-product

The analyses described above are only some of those available to a firm using punched-card data processing. The variety, type, and frequency of analyses will depend, of course, on how comprehensively the firm has applied punched-card methods. Although these analyses may be regarded as by-products of the various procedures, they are, in fact, a main justification for installing a punched-card system. Because they provide management with information essential to the improved control and planning of the company's operations, these analyses must be management's first concern in contemplating the conversion to punched cards. Management must decide what it needs in the way of system by-products, therefore, before it decides on the system itself.

Nevertheless, management has to strike some sort of balance between the analyses it would like to have and the practical limits of the system. It cannot expect a full array of analyses touching every phase of the business from a system handling only order processing and invoicing. Nor, even if it envisages a comprehensive installation, should management overindulge itself in analyses. There have been many cases of punched-card systems producing indigestible quantities of analyses that sat idly on executive desks while management went on grappling with control and planning problems armed only with luck and hunch.

Deciding on what analyses are needed requires that management establish at the outset certain firm objectives governing the control and planning of the company's operations. Having set these objectives, it must then decide what analyses will help it accomplish the objectives. In making this decision, management should be prepared to adopt what may be a drastically different attitude: the attitude of *managing by exception*. It should conceive of analyses designed to report or signal where operations are failing to meet or fulfill the established objectives. The adoption of such an attitude will help prevent the multiplication of analyses to the point where they are never used, let alone heeded. Finally, having decided which analyses are essential, management can examine the firm's data processing methods to discover if they are capable of providing the required analyses.

7

When Is a Punched-card System Feasible?

Many attempts have been made to set up arbitrary guides to help management decide if a punched-card system is feasible for a particular business. These guides use such factors as numbers of transactions, lines of billing per day, number of employees, and numbers of postings to ledgers. Some of these guides may be helpful in giving management a quick rule of thumb as to the size of firm that can effectively use punched-card data processing, but generally they are unreliable in helping management decide on the *kind* of punched-card installation best suited to a firm's individual requirements or even if punched cards are feasible at all. Such a decision is influenced by factors that cannot possibly be embraced by charts or tables. These factors include not only the many characteristics which distinguish one company from all others but also the course of action management intends taking to improve profit performance. A well-organized, thorough *methods study* will give these factors the attention they deserve and furnish management with a means of judging if punched-card data processing is feasible for the firm.

Profit Objectives and Present Methods

The course of action which management intends taking to improve profit performance will be governed by specific objectives. In Chapter 1, it was suggested that management establish profit objectives to guide its control and planning of the firm's operations. These objectives have been defined as the performance goals that management sets for those functions or departments which are most important for their actual or potential contribution to the net profits of the business. In many firms, the choice of a profit objective is fairly obvious: greater sales effort, improved control over production costs, lower inventory investment, and so on. These companies are of such a size that management can single out the function or department capable of making the greatest contribution to profit. In larger companies, the decision on profit objectives might be considerably more involved, necessitating much consultation and study. Nevertheless, in either case, the reason for choosing the objectives is the same: to assure that management effort will produce the most profitable results.

Once it has decided on profit objectives and on the reports needed to accomplish the objectives, management can then appraise the adequacy of present clerical methods:

1. Are present methods capable of furnishing all the reports required?

2. Are the reports which are now available relevant to the chosen objectives?

3. Are these reports current? Are they accurate?

4. Does the preparation of any report entail overtime on the part of the clerical staff? If so, how much overtime?

5. Can any report be prepared without disturbing normal routines?

6. Which reports are patently unnecessary? Which reports duplicate each other?

7. Do the reports presently available contain breakdowns required for management action? Do they reveal the facts management needs for effective action?

8. Would any good management purpose be served by having certain reports sooner?

By asking questions like these, management can form a good idea of the capacity of the present data processing system. Preliminary investigation might show that, with minor modifications or improvements, present methods can furnish the reports required. The next question is: But at what cost? At this point, management could well request a general estimate of the overtime costs involved in the preparation of certain reports.

In addition, the cost of late reports should not be ignored. For example, what are the consequences of a report on raw material valuation always being late? Can the firm *afford* a clerical system that is unable to furnish this critical information promptly?

This preliminary look at present methods in relation to the data processing requirements established by the objectives is by no means conclusive. Its purpose is merely to alert management to the most obvious weaknesses in its present system. Whether or not this system should be replaced by punched cards (or any other system) can be decided only after a thorough methods study. This study may show that modifications in the present system will make it adequate for the firm's requirements. In any event, the study should be undertaken with the purpose of finding out if punched cards are feasible. This will serve to give the study some focus in the minds of those making it.

The Methods Study: A Team Effort

As a general rule, in most companies not yet using automatic data processing the responsibility for clerical procedures is variously divided among a number of different department heads: comptroller, treasurer, credit manager, production manager, sales manager, office manager. These companies are usually not of a size to employ full-time methods personnel. Who, then, can handle the analysis of the present system and investigate the possibility of applying punched-card methods?

The answer is that this task should be handled by a designated individual working with the assistance of a manufacturer of punched-card equipment. The equipment manufacturer will supply the technical knowledge of his machines, and the person designated by the company will furnish information on objectives and procedures. Together, they will study present methods and design a punched-card system suitable to the firm's requirements. The most successful punched-card installations have been the result of this *team effort*.

Company Member of the Team. The company's representative should be familiar with various department operations, the data processing requirements of each, and the over-all objectives of management. He should have the ability to analyze operating procedures and be open-minded, inventive, and tactful in dealing with supervisors and other employees who may feel their job security is threatened by the consideration of a new system.

If the company is fortunate enough to have such a person, there should be no question that his assignment to the methods study outweigh his normal duties. He may be the firm's comptroller, assistant treasurer, office manager, assistant general manager, or vice-president; the title will depend on the size of the company. It is best that he be a member of the middle-management group, with easy access to top management. If such a person is not available, the company (depending on its size) might do well to hire someone with the desired qualifications, preferably with some data processing experience.

To whomever it selects to handle the methods study project, top management should be ready to give unstinting support. It should be ready to back up his decisions and should accord him a fairly wide latitude so that he can deal adequately with intracompany jealousies. But some member of the top-management group should be named as this person's continual contact so that top management is apprised at all times of the progress of the study.

Selecting the Equipment Manufacturer. Once the company has decided who will take charge of the methods study, a manufacturer of punched-card equipment can be approached to assist with the study. The firm should choose its partner carefully. A manufacturer of business machines has usually more to sell than the equipment itself; he is selling a critically important data processing method, one which must be hand-tailored to the firm's requirements. Consequently, it is to the manufacturer's interest to work with the prospective user in developing the system best suited to his requirements. Nonetheless, the prospective user should find out for himself what the manufacturer can offer on the following points.

MAINTENANCE. What is the reputation of the equipment manufacturer for the servicing of its machines? How do other firms in the area or in the same type of business feel about the service this manufacturer renders? What is the type and caliber of maintenance personnel? Are they readily available?

TRAINING. What kind of training program will be offered for machine operators and for supervisory and executive personnel? Where will the training be conducted? Again, what is the opinion of other users?

CUSTOMER ASSISTANCE. What type of technical and specialized assistance is available for the planning, installation, and continuing progress of the punched-card system? What has been the experience of other firms with the equipment manufacturer?

Equipment Manufacturer's Member of the Team. Having satisfied itself that one particular manufacturer is best qualified to help it with its data processing problems, the company asks that a representative initiate the methods study. The sales representatives of most equipment manufacturers have been carefully selected and trained to make recommendations on the use of their company's machines. Also, they have had extensive experience in adapting the equipment to a variety of businesses and conditions. As salesmen, they are naturally "positive thinkers" and, therefore, anxious to persuade a prospect to install their particular units. Nevertheless, the fact that most punched-card data processing systems are installed on a rental or purchase-option basis is a good guarantee against misrepresentation, overselling, and "blue-sky" (versus factual) recommendations. The manufacturer's representative is not inclined, therefore, to sell an unsatisfactory system that can land back on his hands. Not only would time, effort, and considerable expense be wasted, but the manufacturer's reputation would suffer.

From this representative, then, the company may expect expert assistance through all stages up to and after the installation. From the company, the representative expects time and cooperation sufficient for him to make a thorough appraisal of its requirements, after which an intelligent recommendation can be made.

How the Methods Study Is Made

Strictly speaking, the concern of the joint team should not be an analysis of present procedures in the literal sense. What is being sought, rather, is evidence to justify the installation of a punched-card system. Those conducting the methods study will review present methods only to establish the *source, flow,* and *use* of data. When this information is placed alongside the requirements of management's objectives, the shortcomings will be seen.

Another very good reason why a too detailed analysis of present methods is inadvisable is that it can unduly influence the design of

UNIVAC APPLICATIONS STUDY

FORM NO.
UI-1569.1

PAGE_____OF_____

INPUT DATA

APPLICATION_____

COMPANY:
APPLICATIONS ANALYST:

APPROVED BY:

DATE:

FORM DESCRIPTION

FORM NO:

NAME:

SOURCE:

FINAL
DISPOSITION:

VOLUME: AVG.   MAX.

DAILY ☐   WEEKLY ☐   SEMI-MO. ☐   MONTHLY ☐   OTHER _____

FIELD DESCRIPTION

FIELD NAME	% OCCURR.	CHARACTERS		USED BY	REF. CHART STEP NO. (5)	REFER TAPE NO.	COMMENTS
		AVG.	MAX.				

(Present System columns: FIELD NAME, % OCCURR., CHARACTERS AVG./MAX., USED BY, REF. CHART STEP NO. (5); UNIVAC SYSTEM columns: REFER TAPE NO., COMMENTS)

RRISH 16576

FIG. 7-1. A Remington Rand form for recording details of various data (input) entering a procedure.

the proposed punched-card system. Present procedures grew out of entirely different data processing methods. Thus, it is better to tailor the punched-card system to management's objectives than to make it a carbon copy of present methods.

Working together, the methods study team can study the operation of present procedures to determine volumes, how exceptions are handled, and how corrections and adjustments are made. An excellent assignment for the company's member of the team would be the preparation of a write-up of the present system and the collection of sample records and reports and other pertinent facts.

Here is some of the information which a methods study should disclose:

Volume figures — Guesswork or estimates should not be used; if actual figures are not available as part of normal control procedures, a spot check should be made to obtain counts for average and peak-level operations. Typical requirements are the following:

• Number of documents and entries per document (line items, operations, etc.) and per day
• Number of items or part numbers: how produced, packaged, and sold
• Number of units of measure (pieces, hundreds, thousands, pounds, feet, etc.)
• Number of customers
• Number of salesmen
• Number of employees: hourly, salaried, piecework
• Number of piecework rates
• Number of distributions per day
• Number of deductions from payroll daily: withholding, FICA, Blue Cross, Blue Shield, etc.

Accounting periods — Ending dates, cutoff dates, etc.
Pricing or discount schedules — Discount categories, pricing practices (net or list-and-discount).
Terms of payment.
Inventory turnover — Minimum inventory requirements.
Warehousing procedures — Receiving and disbursing.
Sample records — Prepare sample documents containing typical entries, adjustment entries, etc.

UNIVAC APPLICATION STUDY

FORM NO.
91-1529.2

PAGE____ OF ____

OUTPUT DATA (REPORTS & LISTINGS)

APPLICATION____

COMPANY:

APPLICATIONS ANALYST: | APPROVED BY: | DATE:

FORM DESCRIPTION

FORM NO: | NAME:

PREPRINTED FORM ☐ LISTING ☐ REPORT ☐ PAPER SIZE:

NO. OF COPIES: | DISTRIBUTION:

LINES PER PAGE: AVG. MAX. | NO. OF PAGES: AVG. MAX.

PREPARED ON: | DAILY ☐ WEEKLY ☐ SEMI-MO. ☐ MONTHLY ☐ OTHER____

FIELD DESCRIPTION

FIELD NAME	PRESENT SYSTEM				PROPOSED SYSTEM	
	% OCCURR.	CHARACTERS		REF. CHART STEP NO. (S)	REF. TAPE NO.	COMMENTS
		AVG.	MAX.			

RRBH 18278

Fig. 7-2. A form to record details of output data for reports and listings.

Coding classifications presently in use.

Data recording requirements — Number of positions needed to record alphabetical descriptions, customers' names, maximum quantities, etc.

If it will help the methods study team, a flow chart of present procedures can be prepared to show graphically the source and use of data in the firm. It should be stressed again, however, that this chart should not be considered in any way a blueprint for the new system. Unless the clerical methods of a firm are unusually complex, the study team can get along without spending undue time on a detailed flow chart.

Present Costs. As the present procedures are evaluated by the team, the present costs can also be accumulated. Information on the costs of clerical and supervisory personnel, equipment, and supplies should be itemized, as current job write-ups are seldom available in most companies. The most satisfactory way to develop these present costs is to secure a list of employees by department. This list should include rates of pay and information on past overtime. The duties of each person can then be reviewed with the most immediate supervisor and the individuals involved. (Surprisingly, very few supervisors are aware of all that those working under them are doing; a study of present costs serves chiefly, therefore, to pinpoint the duties and responsibilities of members of the clerical staff.)

To any clerical costs should be added an appropriate percentage for fringe benefits. The U.S. Chamber of Commerce publication, "Fringe Benefits 1957," shows that 21.8 per cent is the average of fringe benefits paid by business. This figure varies slightly by region and industry.

Equipment costs should be estimated in terms of current sales prices for comparable equipment and these costs depreciated on the basis normally used by the company. Five to eight years is the normal depreciation period used for office equipment. To these costs should be added annual maintenance and replacement parts costs.

In general, an estimate of present costs will not be a large factor influencing management's decision for or against a punched-card system. As suggested, these costs are useful mainly in establishing whether or not present procedures are efficient, especially in relation to the over-all objectives that management wishes to accomplish. They will alert the methods study team to areas of substandard performance, where clerical effort is too expensive for the results achieved.

The Manufacturer's Proposal

At the conclusion of the study team's examination of the firm's present methods, the manufacturer's representative will prepare a formal proposal showing how punched-card data processing can be applied. The proposal will be a comprehensive review of present methods. It will be essentially a salesman's argument in favor of punched-card methods and must, consequently, be carefully studied by management. But it should be pointed out that, as a result of its

---

•• *Remington Rand*

PROPOSED SYSTEM

Set-Up - Requirements

1. Bill of Material Master Decks containing the related parts cards. Each card will contain Part No., Assembly No., Model No., Description, Quantity required for one assembly and Last Revision Date. Cards will be broken down into their lowest Sub Assembly Division. Example:

    Sub Assembly A - consisting of Parts 1, 2, 3, 4, & 5.

    Sub Assembly B - consisting of Parts 1, 3, 4, 7, etc.

    There will be one extra card for each Sub Assembly, which will contain the Sub Assembly Number and indicate the number of cards required to complete this particular Sub Assembly.

2. Master Decks of parts cards filed by part number. These cards will contain identical information as the B/M File. However, they will be in Part Number sequence rather than Assembly sequence. Should any changes occur such as Engineering, Prices, Location, Description, etc., simply by referring to the Parts File we can readily locate the cards in the particular B/M File as these cards will indicate the assemblies affected by changes. It will actually serve as a cross file which will facilitate changes.

3. Inventory File one card for each part indicating all balances. These cards are filed by Part Number.

4. Master Deck of Vendor Name & Address Cards.

FIG. 7-3. A page from a manufacturer's proposal for a punched-card system.

working with the manufacturer's representative, management should be in a good position to assess the proposal. Further, it is unusual for the joint study to reach the stage of a detailed proposal without management having decided to go ahead with the installation of a punched-card system. In other words, at this stage the feasibility of punched-card data processing for the firm's paperwork has been clearly established.

A typical proposal consists of a letter outlining some important advantages of the proposed system, invariably relating these directly to management's stated objectives. The proposal will also emphasize the advantages of the manufacturer's equipment and why it is suited to the firm's data processing requirements. The main body of the proposal will discuss these requirements in some detail and suggest how the manufacturer's units can be used to meet them.

Having established the need for punched-card equipment, the proposal will then describe a punched-card procedure complete with flow charts, punched-card designs, and verbal descriptions of various processing steps. Finally, it will present estimated one-time costs (tub files, new forms, card cabinets, etc.) and monthly and yearly rental and purchase costs. Salaries of supervisors and clerks will also be included. Some proposals contain suggested bulletins and memos which management should issue to explain the new system to employees. Most proposals show also a timetable advising management of the time required to complete each stage of preinstallation planning.

When Are Punched Cards Feasible?

As stated previously, management can decide if a punched-card system is feasible for its firm only after carefully studying its own data processing requirements. If it finds that present methods are incapable of meeting those requirements, then it can consider the feasibility of punched-card methods. Further study is then needed to turn up evidence justifying the installation of a punched-card system. Thus, punched cards are feasible only if they can be effectively and efficiently applied to the firm's data processing needs and also if they enable management to accomplish its over-all objectives.

8

Planning the Change to Punched Cards — I

Once it has decided that punched-card data processing is feasible for the firm, management faces the task of planning the conversion to the new system. Planning consists of (1) determining the general approach to the projected system and (2) working out the actual details of preinstallation preparations. This chapter deals with the first of these two phases; the following chapter outlines the second.

Although management need not be expected to become directly involved in all the minutiae of planning, it should become positively involved to the extent of making sure that the punched-card system will meet the data processing requirements imposed by the profit objectives. In consequence, management will play a dominant part in planning the total system, deciding the starting point, approving the choice of a supervisor, setting up a conversion timetable, etc.

Management's Part in Planning

Management's involvement with planning the punched-card installation begins the moment it decides on profit objectives and on the kind of information needed to meet the objectives. Common sense dictates, therefore, that management should see that the new system is designed to yield the desired information. Some firms have made the mistake of delegating too much of the planning responsibility to subordinate functionaries, with the result that top management's objectives are overlooked and much time is lost in backtracking to correct aberrations and errors. Management can keep itself apprised of the progress and direction of planning by naming one of its own group to take over-all charge of the planning function. This is invariably the same executive who was responsible for the methods study. His main qualifications are a knowledge of management's objectives, familiarity with the data processing requirements of each department, and easy access to members of top management.

There are other reasons why management must participate in planning.

First, preparation for the new system affects every department in the company and cuts across normal lines of authority. There will be refusals to cooperate and disputes, and there may be organizational changes. Unless those directly in charge of planning have management support, they will be unable to deal adequately and promptly with these exigencies. Management must be ready to settle disagreements, obtain cooperation from everyone affected by the project, and back up any organizational changes that may be necessary to the success of the new system.

Second, the approval of the timetable adopted for the conversion is a major management responsibility. Top management is best fitted to decide which procedures will first be changed over to punched cards and what information is needed immediately. For example, it may be found that a particular type of sales analysis cannot be made available at a specified time following the change to punched cards. In this case, management will have to decide if it can get along without the report for a period, or if the schedule should be advanced to make the preparation of the report possible. As the planning progresses, management will be constantly called upon to modify some of its aims or to alter the conversion timetable to overcome system difficulties.

In this connection, management should insist on periodic reviews of planning progress. It is a good idea to have the executive member of the planning team and the supervisor report to management at regular intervals. In this way, management will know what is being accomplished as the project evolves from early planning stages to eventual completion. There have been instances of serious planning errors because management did not trouble to review each step. Yet, ironically, the same management would not allow a major change to be made in its plant or warehouse operations without keeping itself fully advised on every major detail.

Plan the Total System

For most firms, it is a practical impossibility to install a punched-card system encompassing all procedures. For one thing, most firms prefer to convert only one function or department at a time to gain experience with the new equipment and methods. For another, the cost of a complete change-over is difficult to justify in view of this lack of experience with punched cards.

This apparently piecemeal method of installing punched cards need not be inconsistent with the total-system idea discussed in Chapter 1. But it should be undertaken within the framework of the idea as it has been worked out for the particular firm. In other words, even though it is being applied at only one point at the start, the punched-card installation should be planned to embrace eventually all data processing functions of the firm. If the installation, at the start, is to handle sales analysis, for example, planning should take into consideration its future application to other procedures, such as inventory control, payroll, and invoicing.

The importance of planning a total system becomes clear when it is remembered that a punched-card (or any other automatic data processing) system tends to overemphasize the procedure it is handling. A speaker at an American Management Association seminar made this point:

> If you put your traffic management problem on a machine, you are going to program it in such a way that it is going to give you traffic management answers that will minimize the cost of transportation. This completely ignores the fact that, in many cases, by spending more money for transportation you can reduce your inventory investment. Unless you look at both the inventory management function and the traffic function together . . . you will not get the answer that is in the best interests of the company.

By taking the profit-objective approach, of course, management can anticipate this danger of overemphasis. In the case above, it would have been difficult for traffic management to dominate the data processing system, had management first decided that inventory investment was to be a chief profit objective. Nevertheless, it is not enough only to decide on profit objectives. The total data processing system required by those objectives should be definitely planned; otherwise there will be a tendency to forget original objectives and extend a system to other than the proper and logical applications.

To summarize, the punched-card system must be planned as a total system to (1) avoid maximizing one function at the expense of others, (2) provide for orderly expansion of the system to embrace other functions, and (3) anticipate future data processing requirements as the firm grows.

Decide on a Starting Point

The determination of the point at which to begin the actual conversion to punched cards is the result of assessing several factors. The principal factors are the priority of management's profit objectives and the shortcomings of present methods in providing information to help management achieve those objectives. Along with these, however, should be considered other factors:

• Where can the biggest gains be made with the least effort?
• What has been the experience of other firms with similar data processing problems?
• Does the sequence of handling data demand that one phase of the change-over be started before another because of the source of data?
• Are there impending changes in procedure, policy, or internal organization which will affect data processing requirements?

The first step in deciding on a starting point is to establish what reports management needs to accomplish its chosen objectives. Second, from the methods study, the various sources of data required in the compilation of these reports can be determined.

Assume, for example, that the management of a manufacturing firm has selected the following profit objectives and specified some of the reports required by each:

1. *More accurate sales analysis*
   Analysis by customer

Analysis by product
Analysis by salesman

2. *Improved production control*
   Production schedules
   Efficiency reports
   Idle-time analysis

3. *Lower raw material inventory investment*
   Purchase analysis
   Inventory reports

Assume, further, that management considers lower inventory investment to be the most pressing of the three profit objectives, followed by objectives 1 and 2, in that order. The sources of data for purchase and inventory analyses originate mostly in the purchasing department's procedures. On this basis, it might be thought advisable to make these procedures the starting point for the punched-card system.

On looking more closely into its problem, however, management finds that considerable raw material overstocking is caused by poor production control. But much of the data required for the needed reports in this area originate with the order processing–invoicing procedures. These procedures are also the source of all data needed for more accurate sales analyses. Moreover, the level of clerical efficiency in order processing and invoicing is low. Starting the punched-card system at this point, therefore, will not only take care of two profit objectives—more accurate sales analysis and improved production control—but will represent the biggest gain for the least effort. In time, the system can be expanded to include purchasing procedures, enabling management to begin its attack on its inventory problem.

"Impatience and lack of foresight in selecting the first applications," states an authority on data processing, "can lead to disastrous results." He cautions management against thinking that payroll is the ideal starting point, even for an electronic data processing system. He points out that payroll is too complex for most inexperienced operators, that its critical deadlines allow little cushion for emergencies common to a new system, that errors are costly in terms of employee relations, and that the procedure demands more flexibility than is frequently possible with a new system.

These observations underline heavily the importance of management shaping the decision on the starting point for the punched-card system. Starting the system on the wrong procedures can result in expensive delay and even defeat.

Get the Right Supervisor

Often the major difference between a well-functioning punched-card system and an utter failure is the difference between an able, intelligent supervisor and one who is inept. To the appointment of the supervisor of its machine accounting department management should give the same serious attention it would give to the appointment of a key executive. For, in many ways, the supervisor is indeed a key executive; he is the working link between management's objectives and the system that will provide management with the information to accomplish its objectives.

Unfortunately, many companies choose the supervisor on the basis of seniority, friendship, or other considerations completely unrelated to administrative ability. Top management should have the courage to reject a patently unwise choice, however sentimental or "obligatory" the choice might be.

A supervisor's ineptitude may spring from several causes, but it is most damaging when it springs from (1) an inability to handle people and (2) an inability to analyze situations and make decisions. It must always be remembered that the supervisor plays a dual role. He must be both qualified technically to plan and operate a system and able to supervise the work of others. In hiring a supervisor to help plan the installation of a new system, management sometimes rates his technical qualifications higher than necessary, forgetting that the same man will later be in charge of several persons in a pivotal department. Thus, whether or not he has the intelligence and tact for such an assignment is often overlooked.

IBM, which yearly trains hundreds of supervisors for its customers, says this: "Intelligence and management ability are more important individual assets in a supervisor than technical machine experience. Machine techniques can be learned (at some expense in time and progress), but the other attributes cannot."

Should the supervisor be hired outside the firm, or should a promising employee be trained for the position? Both practices are equally favored. It is not uncommon for smaller businesses to hire experienced machine operators on the outside and appoint them supervisors of their systems. There is nothing wrong with this method, provided, as mentioned above, that the person hired has much more to offer than his machine experience. On the other hand, very many successful punched-card installations have been planned and are managed by employees who were promoted to the position and trained by the equipment manufacturer.

Whichever method is chosen, the choice should be made as soon as possible after the decision to change to punched cards. The knowledge of the firm's procedures and policies that the supervisor gains during the planning stage will be invaluable both to him and to the company after the installation is operating.

Timetable for Change

It would be quite impossible to state flatly how long it takes to convert certain procedures to punched cards. Understandably, every firm's conversion problems are unique, so that even two firms of the same size in the same kind of business would perhaps not complete their respective changes to punched cards within several months of each other. Nonetheless, this does not mean that a strict schedule cannot be drawn up for the change-over. Such a schedule serves to organize the work of everyone connected with the proposed installation.

The six main phases of planning are discussed in more detail in the following chapter, but they are listed chronologically here to show the relative priority of each main phase and, generally, what detail tasks each includes:

1. *Procedure development*
   Coding
   Card design
   Document and report design
   Operational flow charts
   Accounting controls
2. *Machine specifications*
   Machine-load requirements
   Special devices
   Auxiliary supplies and requirements
3. *Employee training*
   Supervisor

  Machine operators
  Card-punch operators
4. *Final stages of planning*
  Site preparation
  Card electroplates
  Prepunched card files
  Control-panel wiring
  Accessory equipment ordering
5. *Procedure manuals*
  Operator's manual
  Supervisor's manual
  General manual
6. *After the installation*
  Work schedules
  Evaluation
  Future planning

Equipment manufacturers warn prospective users of punched-card systems to be, if anything, pessimistic when drawing up a conversion timetable. Says one, "It is an altogether too common mistake to try to accomplish too much in too short a period of time." Thus, the timetable should allow the planners the time necessary to work out the procedures being converted, to check back continually to see that no details are being overlooked, and to solve personnel problems as they arise. The timetable should also be flexible, permitting changes resulting from new policies or ideas.

9

Planning the Change to Punched Cards — II

The detailed planning of a punched-card installation means starting with the basic information turned up by the methods study (see Chapter 7). All that should interest the planners in present methods is the data involved in particular procedures and what use is to be made of the data. Using this information as a foundation, the planners build entirely new procedures tailored to the special demands and characteristics of punched-card equipment. This is not to say that the equipment becomes the sole determinant of the procedures but that the planners must seek to use the equipment in the most efficient and the best way consistent with a firm's data processing requirements. There is little to be gained, therefore, by adapting punched-card methods to existing procedures. A safe guarantee of an installation's success is to plan it as if nothing but the original data and the firm's requirements exist.

Developing the Procedures

The methods study will have disclosed these facts about the data used in the firm's various clerical procedures:

1. *Quantities of data processed:* number of invoices, accounting entries, products, salesmen, customers, etc.

2. *Kinds of data processed:* pricing practices, product specifications, freight allowances, incentive pay scales, etc.

3. *When data are processed:* billing cycle periods, report periods, peak periods, seasonal factors, etc.

4. *Sequence in which data are processed:* dependence of some procedures on others (e.g., are inventory records changed before or after invoicing?)

These facts, together with a knowledge of management's profit objectives and of the firm's operations, provide the planners with the information necessary for building up punched-card procedures. The principal first steps in the development of these procedures are given below.

Forms Design: The record and report forms which served manual methods will not serve machine methods for a number of reasons. Not only will special continuous-feed forms be required for use on the tabulating machine, but many of the source records will have to be redesigned because of different data requirements and arrangement. For example, many firms endeavor to have data placed on a source document in the same sequence as they would be punched into a card, thereby speeding up keypunching. Early attention to forms design is important also because it bears on the number of spaces which can be allotted to various types of data. Further, the information which management desires to be shown on reports will affect the sequence and number of processing steps needed to prepare these reports.

Card Design: Knowing the kinds of data involved in the procedures being converted to punched cards, and also the kind of output (records and reports) desired, the planners can determine what cards will be needed to carry out the procedures. The next step is to work out how data will be recorded in the cards. Space is restricted to the columns available, and, consequently, upon card design rests the next step in procedures development: coding.

Coding: While it depends to a great extent on card design, coding is also a factor affecting card design. The difficult task of formulating an item code, for example, may result in a longer code number than was originally assigned in the card design. It may be necessary, therefore, to modify the card design to accommodate the code.

The coding of the main units of constant and variable data enables the machines to handle them efficiently. Although sorters are able to arrange alphabetical data in sequence, they do so only with many passes of the cards through the machine. But if a numerical code were assigned to each unit of alphabetical data, the sorters can operate in much less time and still arrange the cards in the desired sequence. For example, the name Brown would be assigned, say, a code number of 10, and the name Browne would be assigned the number 11; the sorter could then achieve alphabetical sequence by sorting on numerical sequence.

number of days before delivery of equipment...

120–150 days	90–120 days	60–90 days	60 days and under

PROCEDURES
  begin coding
  chart of operational steps
  accounting controls
 	
CARDS AND FORMS
  design of record and report forms
  design of cards
 	
MACHINE REQUIREMENTS
  determine capacities and need for special devices for all machines
 	
SITE PREPARATION
  floor plan
  weight requirements
  elevator capacity
  door widths
  air conditioning
 	
TRAINING
  management orientation
	PROCEDURES
	  step-by-step development of punched-card method
	
	CARDS AND FORMS
	  design proofs approved
	  cards, forms ordered
	
	SITE PREPARATION
	  electrical outlets
	  lighting
	  soundproofing
	
	TRAINING
	  supervisor
		PROCEDURES
		  detailed operating flow charts completed
		
		AUXILIARY EQUIPMENT
		  card cabinets
		  files
		  desks, tables, chairs
		  manuals, reference equipment
		  miscellaneous equipment
		
		TRAINING
		  machine operators
		  card-punch operators
			PROCEDURES
			  operating manuals
			  work schedules
			  control panels wired
			  dry runs
			  parallel runs
			
			CARDS AND FORMS
			  punch master files
			
			TRAINING
			  management orientation

Fig. 9-1. Timetable for change. Above are estimates of the number of days (before machine delivery) needed to complete the main steps in converting to punched cards. These estimates are a composite of those made by IBM and Remington Rand systems personnel and will naturally vary with conditions encountered by an individual company.

Coding must be preceded by uniform nomenclature and style covering such data as customer's names and addresses, salesmen's names, and item descriptions. In regard to the latter, a general classification of the items sold by a company is first agreed on, and then the various items are grouped within specific categories, leaving sufficient room

	IBM RAMAC 305 Installation Schedule	Personnel Assigned	Personnel Code
	Projects		
1.	Objectives & Schedule	1, 9	DP Coordinator 1
2.	Selection of Personnel	1, 2	Tab Supervisor 2
3.	Site Planning (Preliminary)	1, 9	Programmer 3
4.	Personnel Training	2, 3, 4, 5, 6	Programmer 4
			Key Punch Oper. 5
5.	Input-Volume & Requirements	1, 9	Key Punch Oper. 6
6.	Output-Volume & Requirements	1, 9	Console Oper. 7
	(Inventory)		IBM 9
7.	305 Records (B/M)	1, 9	
	(Cost & Scheduling)		
8.	File Purification		
9.	Reorder point, EOQ concept		
10.	305 Addressing Technique	1, 9	
11.	File Organization	1, 9	
12.	Low Level Coding	1, 9	
13.	Programs–Material Transaction	3, 4, 9	
	Level by level	3, 4, 9	
	Purchase planning	3, 4, 9	
	Order issue	3, 4, 9	
	Status reports	3, 4, 9	
	File Maintenance	3, 4, 9	
14.	File Load Programs	3, 4, 9	
15.	Wire 305 Panels	3, 9	
16.	Prepare for Test	1, 2, 3, 4, 9	
17.	Program Test	3, 4, 7, 9	
18.	Rework Programs	3, 4	
19.	Card & Form Design	2, 3, 4, 9	
20.	Peripheral Equipment Schedule	9	
21.	Timing–All Equipment	9	
22.	Schedule–All Equipment	9	
23.	Review Equipment–Specifications	9	
24.	IBM Review–Region	9	
25.	Order Accessories	1	
26.	Order Panels	1	
27.	Physical Planning (Complete)		
28.	Procedures Manuals	3, 9	
29.	Operations Manuals	1, 2, 4	
30.	305 Installation	All	
31.	File Load	3, 4, 7, 9	
32.	Final Test	All	
33.	Actual Operation	All	

Fig. 9-2. This chart shows the schedule of American Bosch Division for the installation of a Ramac 305. The preinstallation period extended from June to October, during which programmers were trained, master files of constant data were set up and checked, and all personnel affected by the new system were educated. Progressive planning was done through weekly meetings, and at least once a month the coordinator of the conversion program issued a written progress report to the division manager.

in each category for adding new items. Item description and other alphabetical data are, of course, affected by the character-count limit imposed by forms and card designs.

In assigning code numbers, there is often a tendency to attempt a connection between the style of code adopted and the description of an item. For example, the firm may have designated a pipe wrench as W-276-9P-273 in its catalogue. Such a designation is practically impossible to preserve in a machine code. The planners are well advised to scrap previous codes and adopt those which facilitate the handling of data by machines. Employees will be surprisingly quick to recognize and accept the new codes.

IBM has set out six criteria governing the construction of an adequate code.

FLEXIBILITY: The code should provide room for additional entries in sequence. For example, in the case of customers' names, the A's can be assigned code numbers in the 1000 class, B's code numbers in the 2000 class, and so on, but only after it has been determined that these classes will accommodate the anticipated number of names.

SCOPE: The code should be designed to allow expansion to include additional categories. If a firm contemplates adding new product lines, it can set aside certain groups of code numbers for this contingency.

OPERATION: The code should be adequate for all required tabulator segregations. For example, if reports are to be prepared showing the trade classification of each customer, it might be feasible to make this classification part of the customer's account number. Or if the source of supply for each item handled by a firm is to be shown in reports, this can become part of the item code.

CONVENIENCE: The code should be easy to assign. The classification of, for example, the variegated product lines of a merchandising firm, with groups of code numbers reserved for each, will aid in assigning new codes and also in recognizing code number groups.

CONSTRUCTION: The code should have the least possible number of digits consistent with the problem to reduce punching and sorting effort.

IDENTIFICATION: The code should, if possible, facilitate visual identification. Again, the classification of product categories and the assigning of definite groups of numbers to these categories will assist employees in recognizing certain numbers. For example, all wrenches might be coded with numbers beginning 100 and all hammers with numbers beginning 200.

Many companies that have evolved satisfactory codes have delegated the job of coding to employees thoroughly conversant with the items being coded. One company, for example, found that several experienced pricing clerks were well qualified to (1) write out alphabetical descriptions of each item which would fit within a specified character count and (2) assign code numbers to each item according to the type of code decided on by the company's planners and the equipment manufacturer's representative.

The employees chosen for the coding job should be relieved of their regular duties so that they can work without interruptions. Since code numbers are the main entry into the punched-card system, they must be given the highest priority in planning.

Equipment manufacturers have prepared several booklets which are helpful to a company setting out on a coding project. The company should also check with other companies to discover suitable coding methods.

Accounting Controls: As described previously (Chapter 4), accounting controls are necessary as a common-sense precaution against error and fraud. As such, they must be provided for in the procedure, and preferably in the early stages of procedure development, since they will affect the procedure and (in some cases) the equipment.

Flow Charts: As the punched-card procedure is evolved, operational flow charts detailing each step are drawn. The finished flow charts begin usually as a series of diagrams blocking in the general procedure.

Each of a series of flow charts will show the individual steps in greater detail. Each step indicated on the charts is numbered and explained verbally alongside. Later, after the procedure has been carefully checked, the revised charts and write-ups become part of the procedure manual (see below).

The equipment manufacturers will provide flow-chart templates and suggested flow-charting and procedure methods.

Machine Requirements

The facts disclosed by the methods study will have provided the manufacturer's representative with sufficient information to specify the machines needed for the installation. Besides selecting units of the desired capacities, he will also provide for special devices in the case of certain machines. The accounting machine, for example, might have to be fitted with special type bars to print fractions, or a card punch might have to be fitted with an offset card-stacking device. Many of these technical details can, however, be resolved long after the purchase contract has been signed by the customer.

Employee Training

Chronologically, arrangements for employee training are among the first planning steps taken. Particularly is this so with the supervisor and some key management people who will be directly affected by the installation. Other clerical workers and machine operators (including card-punch operators) are trained later in the schedule. The timetable and other details of employee training are discussed in the next chapter.

Final Stages of Planning

The final stages of planning cover such details as site preparation, making of electroplates for the punched cards, prepunching the required card files, wiring machine control panels, and ordering and installing accessory equipment.

Site Preparation. A punched-card installation is best housed in its own room. Although manufacturers are reducing the noise level of the various units, machine operators contend that isolation from the general office area is more conducive to concentration and accuracy. At any rate, since many of the card files contain the company's confidential records, they should be kept under close and constant supervision in one location.

In selecting a site for the installation, the planner should keep several points in mind. Chief among these is floor load capacity; this should be at least 100 pounds per square foot to bear the weight of the average installation, but this requirement can be covered individually with the manufacturer. The area selected for the installation should have doors wide enough to allow the units to be moved in and out easily. Also, if the site is to be above the first floor, elevator capacity should be considered.

If the machines are to be installed in a room adjoining the general office, soundproofing will be necessary. Air conditioning of the site is desirable, especially in high-humidity regions where irreparable damage to cards could result. An electrical contractor should be called in to check present wiring and to provide extra outlets for the various machines. Adequate lighting should be furnished in all work areas.

There are no standard plans governing machine-room floor layout, as this is determined by the space available for the installation; but care should be taken to keep traffic patterns clear of obstructions and to cut down unnecessary walking between various machines, such as between the tub files and card punches.

Card Electroplates. When designs for the various punched cards have been approved, printing plates are made so that column headings and other information can be shown on the cards. These plates

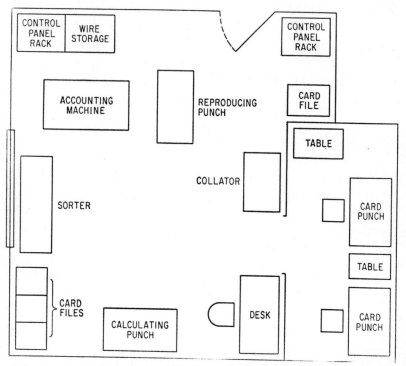

Fig. 9-3. Floor layout of a machine accounting department. Note walls setting off the card-punch area to keep down noise level.

are good for many thousands of impressions and are relatively inexpensive. The equipment manufacturer normally arranges to have them made.

Card Files. Among the final preinstallation preparations is the punching of the various master cards containing constant data, for example, customer master cards. It is not unusual to have a card punch moved in ahead of the other machines and to have a newly trained card-punch operator assigned to this task.

Control-panel Wiring. When a punched-card procedure has been worked out in detail, the control panels are wired and tested for the various machines. It is usually desirable to have the more complex panels wired and retained on a semipermanent basis, with a cover protecting the wires. This cover can be removed for any changes that might become necessary due to changes in procedure, report requirements, etc. Normally, it is best for the company's supervisor to wire the control panels so that he has a complete knowledge of operations and can readily make changes.

Accessory Equipment. Tub files, card cabinets, desks, tables, etc., must be ordered for the new installation. The equipment manufacturer's representative can advise the company on what types of units will be needed. Normally this equipment is not rented, but Remington Rand has announced rental plans covering some units.

The Procedure Manuals

When the procedures being converted to punched cards have been thoroughly checked and the flow charts and write-ups revised, the supervisor has the responsibility of preparing manuals explaining each procedure in full detail. He can prepare three such manuals: operators', manager's, and general. According to IBM, these manuals are necessary for five reasons:

1. To enable operators to set up their machines and to complete a job without supervisory assistance.

2. To provide a permanent record of job requirements in the event of illness, vacations, and operator turnover.

3. To provide assembled facts for simplifying corrections and improvements of procedures.

4. To facilitate the duties of managing the personnel, machines, and work of a punched-card installation.

5. To allow for executive understanding and control of the punched-card data processing department.

IBM and the other equipment manufacturers furnish a variety of printed forms to help supervisors assemble these manuals. For example, the operators' manual includes sheets in which each job is explicitly described (Figure 9-4). The reverse side of a previous job sheet can be used for the matching flow chart illustrating the procedure step. Other printed forms are available for describing over-all clerical procedures and for detailing setup data for each machine for various jobs

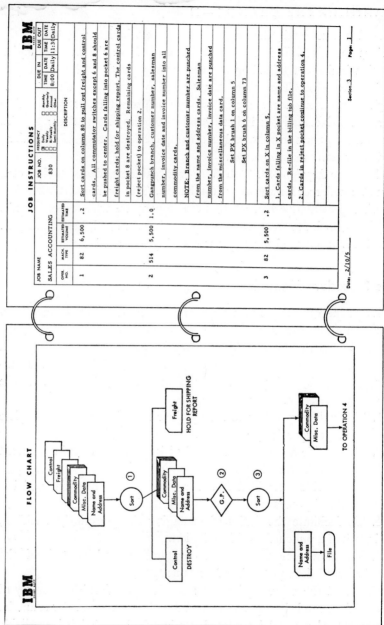

Fig. 9-4. Pages from procedure manual, showing flow charts on one side and narrative job instructions on facing page.

128

(Figure 9-5). As can be seen from the illustrations, an operators' manual is complete to the final detail. The supervisor has the further responsibility of keeping the manual continually up to date.

The supervisor's own (or manager's) manual includes written information on due-in and due-out requirements covering various reports, over-all operational flow charts, code lists, charts showing monthly machine use—indeed, all the basic facts significant to the supervisor's task of managing and planning the work of his department. A general manual, containing sample copies of reports and source data together with general flow charts of major applications, is frequently useful in keeping management and others informed about the system.

After the Installation

Critical to any punched-card installation are the first few months of operation. This is a time of testing, not only for the new system,

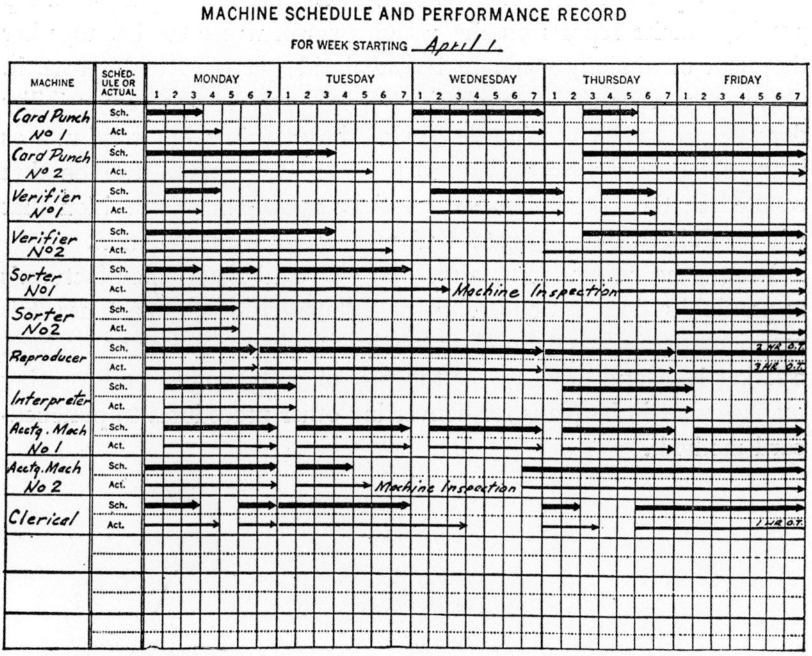

Fig. 9-5. The supervisor keeps this record, showing the master schedule for each machine and its actual performance.

but also for the supervisor and his management. It will be a time of testing, too, for all the planning prior to the installation. If the planning has been slipshod in any major respect, the consequences will be reaped in the first few months. Normally, if planning has been conscientiously carried out, any oversights that appear are minor and are easily corrected during testing or soon after the procedure is changed over to punched cards.

Under the supervisor's direction, the operations of the new system can be so coordinated and controlled as to minimize difficulties during the first months. First, with the help of management, he can clearly establish what work must be done and in what sequence. Second, he can determine work loads by keeping records of the quantity of documents, cards, and reports processed. Third, knowing how the work load fluctuates from time to time and job to job, he can establish work schedules to achieve the best use of machines and operators. Fourth, through proper attention to accounting and other controls, he can maintain accuracy in the installation's work and see that all procedures are performed correctly.

For its part, management should insist that the supervisor keep precise, concise reports on the system's performance so that together they can continually evaluate it and decide on ways to improve it. Once more, it must be emphasized that management's responsibility does not end with the installation of the machines but continues as long as the system exists. Just as it was management's decision that resulted in the installation, so it will be management's decision that will result in the improvement and extension of the installation.

It may be pointed out, also, that the equipment manufacturer's responsibility does not end with the installation of the machines. His representative will keep in close touch with the supervisor and others, offering help and advice over the first difficult months and assisting management in its plans for converting other procedures to punched-card methods.

10

Punched Cards and People

The merest hint that management is considering a punched-card installation will ignite a brush-fire of speculation among all employees and antagonism among many. There will be rumors that office automation will throw numbers of workers out of jobs. Some employees in key posts will resent a new method that threatens their positions and authority. Unless management tells employees from the very start how punched-card data processing will affect them and their jobs, it will meet mounting resistance, which will frustrate planning efforts. From the very outset, management should recognize the fact that a punched-card system will make its influence felt on every job in the office and beyond. Some employees will have to be retrained and others shifted to other tasks because their present ones are no longer needed. Many jobs will remain the same except for slight changes in routine to fit in with the new system. Management's responsibility is to see that these changes are handled with the least possible disruption and discontent.

Does a Punched-card System Cost Jobs?

One of management's objectives in installing punched-card data processing is to achieve greater efficiency in clerical operations. Efficiency can, however, mean different things to different managements, depending on conditions prevailing in their respective offices. To the management of a firm that has over the years progressively updated its equipment and methods, the conversion to punched-card methods may be only another inevitable step forward. Such a firm has possibly been able to keep productive employees to a minimum, and it envisions punched-card methods as a means of making these employees even more productive. But there are many firms whose office operations have fallen so far behind the growth of the company and management's demand for essential control and planning information that management regards punched-card methods as a long-sought opportunity to eliminate great numbers of superfluous employees.

Frankly, there are no set answers to the question: Do punched cards cost jobs? Any answer must depend on a number of factors peculiar to the individual firm. If the firm is one in which all its operations are clerical—an insurance company, for example—automatic data processing can have startling results so far as numbers of employees are concerned. If, on the other hand, the firm is a manufacturing concern of a type where order processing and billing consume little office time, a punched-card system might have little effect on the number of persons employed in the office. It is for management to decide whether a punched-card system will have a marked effect on office employment.

Actually, a great many companies installing punched cards have experienced either or both of these results:

1. Low-grade or marginal employees performing routine filing and other tasks are usually no longer needed, since much of the filing is taken over by the machine accounting department.

2. Many of the employees who would normally quit or go into retirement need not be replaced.

It has also been the experience of many average-sized firms that, following the installation of punched cards, the clerical staff increases moderately. This is principally because, as the new system is extended to more and more procedures and management makes more and more demands on the system, more employees are required both in and outside the system. This trend can be understandably disturbing to management, but it will be found that, in terms of what the system is producing, each of these employees is more productive than would be the case under a conventional system.

As stated previously, the exact effect of a punched-card system will depend largely on the conditions obtaining in the individual firm. It is management's responsibility to assess this situation, and to decide what steps should be taken to deal with the employees. If, because of the nature of the company's operation, a main objective behind the installation is to eliminate numbers of employees, then it must choose its course accordingly. If, in the interests of internal harmony, it wishes to reassure its employees regarding the installation of the new system, then management should consider steps needed to educate employees to the new system and to solicit their cooperation in making the conversion.

Getting Employees to Accept the New System

Everyone is in favor of progress—somewhere else. When progress intrudes itself on one's own life or locality or routine, it is regarded in a highly personal and prejudiced way. The homeowner who grumbles about weekend traffic jams is often the first to sign the petition protesting the expressway planned to pass half a mile from his house. The skilled billing clerk is no different when she hears of a new punched-card installation which threatens to eliminate her job. A writer in the *Harvard Business Review* reports that even employees in the punched-card data processing department can respond the same way when a computer installation is projected:

> In one of the companies studied, the people in the computer room suspected the tab machine group of obstructionist tactics in preparing the cards. Failure to meet deadlines, frequent errors, and sometimes downright refusal to carry out certain requests, as a protest "that they can't be done that way," characterizes the performance of these people, whose average time with the company was ten years.[1]

Unless management tells employees from the very start how a punched-card system will affect them and their jobs, it will meet mounting resistance that will frustrate later planning efforts. The office grapevine will sprout with numberless rumors of layoffs, job changes, demotions, and all manner of resentments against the new system. An expert in personnel relations declares that, since the grapevine cannot

[1] Ida R. Hoos, "When the Computer Takes Over the Office," *Harvard Business Review,* July–August, 1960, p. 108.

be abolished, management's best step is to give it reliable information to feed on. At the earliest opportunity, therefore, the member of management handling planning should hold a meeting to explain to employees what the new system is, how it works, and why the firm is planning to install it. This should also be an opportunity for employees to ask questions, so that their worst fears can be put to rest, and to find out exactly what the new system will mean to their own jobs. A conducted tour to an actual installation has been found by some companies a highly effective method of education.

In the various media that management uses to communicate with employees (company bulletins, publications, notice boards), it can carry out a continuing program of education to precede and parallel the methods study:

1. It can explain why a thorough analysis of the present system is needed and how each employee can cooperate with it.

2. At intervals during preinstallation planning, it can explain to employees what is being done and what has yet to be done.

3. It can describe the opportunity of enrolling in training courses and taking jobs as machine operators.

4. As the system begins to evolve, management can explain it to employees in terms of their jobs and the benefits they will derive from it.

5. Management can meet frequently with supervisors of key employees to see that they are cooperating with the planning efforts.

6. It can invite employees to submit suggestions in connection with the new system.

The installation of punched cards poses a particular problem with older, experienced workers. Frequently, these employees have come to handle a fair degree of responsibility and will naturally resist a system that threatens to abridge it. Frequently, too, many of these older workers do not look kindly on the idea of taking routine jobs in the machine accounting room, even though, as a result of receiving training, they may receive more salary. They are unwilling to give up privileges or prestige that has grown up around their previous positions. It might be parenthetically pointed out here that the problems of the older worker have little to do with ability to learn—the latest studies prove a high learning ability—but rather with unwillingness to give up a certain status.

Some firms have solved the problem of the older worker by retaining them in substantially the same job but dealing with exception procedures that cannot by handled by the punched-card system. Other firms have been pleasantly surprised to find many older employees willingly accepting training to take jobs in the system.

The prospect of being upgraded in both status and salary by being trained as machine operators is a powerful inducement to many employees. But management should not oversell upgrading as a means of buying employee cooperation or harmony cheaply. The novelty of a new system soon wears off, and those employees who were led to expect too much from their training find themselves doing repetitive, demanding work. A publication of the U.S. Department of Labor points out:

> Operators of most office machines must be able to adapt themselves to routine, repetitive work and to the noise made by the machines. Operators of machines such as keypunch, calculating, billing machines are seated at desks most of the day, while operators of tabulating machines may have to stand for long periods.

Employees should not be given the impression, therefore, that the installation of punched-card equipment will result in "glamor" jobs. But they can quite rightly look forward to jobs that are very probably more responsible and exacting than those currently held.

Getting Executive Acceptance

The above suggestions on obtaining employee acceptance apply even more forcibly in the case of managers and supervisory heads. In addition, as the experience of many companies has shown, every effort should be made to have these employees participate actively in the actual planning of the installation. Naturally, it would be absurd to appoint every subordinate executive or supervisor to the planning group; nevertheless, where the planning of the system involves his section or department, the manager should be included in the deliberations of the planning group. Further, these persons should be frankly informed of any change in their responsibilities resulting from the installation of the new system. For example, in a manufacturing company, the purchasing director was told that the projected punched-card installation would take over much of his department's inventory control chores. In consequence, several of his typists and inventory control clerks would be transferred to other departments. The purchasing director was prepared to resist this change until he was informed, during a series of meetings with the group planning the new system, that he would be henceforth exercising executive responsibilities regarding inventory control instead of those of an office manager overseeing a number of clerical workers. Had he been ignored by the planning group, however, the purchasing director might have created difficulties for both himself and the company.

In general, executive acceptance can be obtained by (1) inviting department heads and their assistants to participate in determining the basic company objectives underlying the new system and (2) enlisting their active help in evolving the new system itself. In this way, these members of middle management will be made aware of and have some say in deciding on any changes in executive responsibilities arising from the new system. Cooperation in the preparation and use of new management reports and the revision of existing reports will also be more easily obtained. Of great importance is the fact that the new system will be kept *within the context of the company;* that is, the danger of some managers arriving at hasty conclusions about the impact of a new system on their functions will be avoided. They will be less inclined to take the alarmist view of automatic data processing once they have taken part in its application to their own jobs.

Certainly not all the decisions finally made regarding the new system will satisfy everyone. But this is a condition common to business life and persists whether or not automatic data processing is involved. Every member of management must at some stage reconcile himself to decisions with which he does not agree. Nevertheless, the more those in charge of the new project involve subordinate members of management, the more they can reduce the area of disagreement and of ultimate disaffection.

Training Employees for Punched Cards

As soon as a decision is made to go ahead with a punched-card installation, arrangements are made with the equipment manufacturer to train machine operators, the supervisor, and certain key members of management. The equipment manufacturers conduct large-scale educational programs, with instruction ranging from keypunching to computer programming to executive orientation. There is no charge for customers' employees attending these schools; the only cost to the customers is for transportation and employees' salary and expenses.

The members of management most directly concerned with the installation are usually the first to be trained. They are given orientation courses (usually a week long) at a manufacturer's school. Next, the supervisor receives specialized training of longer duration. Finally, two or three months before the installation of equipment, the key-punch and machine operators are trained; this instruction is often given locally at an equipment manufacturer's branch facility. The manufacturer will conduct aptitude tests among the company's employees to find those most suitable for training.

The Supervisor: Key Man

The success of many a punched-card installation has been decided by the caliber of its supervisor or manager. Although something can be said about the wisdom of placing too much reliance in one man, the fact remains that a competent supervisor is as essential to a well-functioning system as a competent superintendent is to a well-functioning factory.

Reference has been made previously to the desirability of hiring a supervisor (or promoting someone from within the firm to the position) who has much more to offer than only proficiency with the machines. Such a person should, of course, be qualified in the technical operation of the machine accounting department, but he should also be able to work well with the employees in his charge and with members of management. If he has serious shortcomings in the latter respect, the effectiveness and efficiency of the installation can suffer as a result. In addition to his technical qualifications, therefore, a supervisor should possess most of the following attributes:

• *Ability to understand the firm's operations.* The supervisor should be one who will interest himself in the company's business, its products or services, and its markets. He should also concern himself with trends and problems affecting the business.

• *Ability to understand management methods.* Since his department is the crossroads or exchange for the business data flowing through the company, the supervisor should familiarize himself with the various ways in which management carries out its control and planning functions.

• *Ability to understand company objectives.* A supervisor should find out the objectives that management has established, so that he can appreciate the significance of the various reports prepared by his department. Also, with a knowledge of objectives, he will be in a position to suggest improvements in report content.

• *Ability to train employees.* From the moment a machine accounting department starts operating, the need for training begins. A competent supervisor will set up and be prepared to carry out a training schedule to provide for employee turnover and the introduction of new procedures and machines.

• *Ability to plan ahead.* The supervisor should be constantly aware of the demands that the company's growth will make on his department. He should keep in touch with key members of management to stay abreast of future data processing requirements and should work with them in planning future procedures.

• *Ability to innovate.* He should be continually alert to new developments and methods in his own field, but a supervisor should also be receptive to the ideas of others. He should never build a wall around his department so that it becomes unapproachable to persons with valid ideas. A good supervisor cannot be an "empire builder" and a company builder at one and the same time.

In a well-managed company, the conversion to punched-card data processing should not create insoluble personnel problems. If management encounters unusually stiff resistance to the projected change-over, there is undoubtedly something more basic at fault, something that would eventually come to the surface regardless of punched cards. Wherever this kind of resistance appears, therefore, management should endeavor to find out what the real trouble is. The fact of converting to a new method of data processing should not be held responsible for difficulties that arise elsewhere.

11

The Seven Imperatives of Punched Cards

The planning and successful application of punched-card data processing is largely a matter of give and take. So that it can *give* management the quality of information required for profitable operation of the business, a punched-card system *takes* the utmost in management's persistence and patience. Thus, once management has met the system's demands, it can expect substantial benefits. It is when management fails or refuses to meet these demands or attempts to circumvent them that it ends up with a system that is ineffectual or inadequate. The foregoing chapters have discussed the demands and how management might satisfy them. At this point, these imperatives of punched-card data processing are recapitulated. These are the seven basic rules that management should observe in approaching automatic data processing. Together they add up to the attitude that management should adopt in a climate of intensifying competition and climbing costs.

Imperative 1: Take a Fresh Look at the Office

Management's pressing need, in even the smallest business, for prompt, timely information relating to the critical phases of the firm's operations confers on the office a pivotal function, that of providing analyses that are significant to the control and planning efforts. Because it can help management make decisions that can augment the firm's profits, the office can reasonably be regarded as a profit-making function in its own right. With the advent of punched cards and other automatic data processing methods, the office has ceased to be a non-productive, dead-weight cost. As a matter of fact, as a result of these new methods, the office has ceased to be a mere area bounded by four walls. The new methods have enabled the total-system idea to take hold, so that the influence of the office pervades the whole business.

Even though a conventional office may presently be furnishing management with required decision-making information, its inefficiencies and wastes cannot be ignored. Management must ask itself: "Are we getting enough mileage out of our present office cost?" The satisfactory answer to this question will come only after a detailed study of methods used to process and analyze data generated by the firm's operations.

A fresh look at the office will consist in determining if it is functioning at the least possible cost consistent with management's need for profit-making information.

Imperative 2: Establish Profit Objectives

Rising costs of operation have made management acutely aware of profits. The first step toward evolving a data processing system that will give management profit-making information is the establishment of profit objectives. This entails a fundamental examination of the company's character, markets, and potential to discover what functions or departments are most critical in terms of their contributions to profit.

Having made this examination, management establishes goals, or profit objectives, enabling each function or department to make its fullest contribution to profit. A chief advantage of establishing profit objectives is that various operations of the firm are brought into proper balance with one another. The dangers inherent in one function or department optimizing its performance at the possible expense of another can be avoided. Profit objectives impress on management the interdependence of operations and thus can result in improved control and planning of the business.

Profit objectives are important to a data processing system because they are, in fact, the main objectives to be served by the system. There cannot be one set of objectives for the firm as a whole and another for the data processing system. Since the system will provide the information that management needs to achieve the objectives, the system's emphasis and design will be shaped by the objectives.

As a prominent consultant has said, "It is very difficult . . . to set up procedures designed to help top management accomplish something, if management itself does not know what it is trying to do."

Imperative 3: Decide on Information Needed to Achieve Objectives

Having established its profit objectives, management can decide what information it needs to accomplish those objectives. At this point, management can also measure the effectiveness of present clerical methods, discovering whether or not they are capable of providing the information required. If it finds that present methods are unequal to providing the needed reports, management is justified in investigating alternative systems.

Imperative 4: Look for Profit Improvement First

Management is cautioned against considering a new data processing system purely on the basis of how much it can reduce clerical costs. A system's real effectiveness is measured by its ability to furnish information enabling management to improve the firm's profit position and not by its ability to secure clerical savings. Although clerical savings are admittedly important, they should not dominate management's approach to a new system.

Imperative 5: Management Must Take an Active Part in Planning

Even though it involves many technicalities beyond management's inclination or even capabilities, the planning of a punched-card installation demands management's active participation at every stage. Not only should the head of the company's planning group be a member of management, but he should have ready access to all members of top management. And he should be fully conversant with management's profit objectives—preferably to the extent of having had a part in establishing them.

Management itself should insist on regular reports of planning progress and on passing final approval on the conversion timetable adopted. Management should also have final approval on the choice of the starting point for the installation as well as on the sequence in which other procedures are to be brought into the new system.

The moment management loses control over the planning of the installation, it abrogates a basic prerogative: determining the kind of information it requires for the effective control and planning of the business.

Imperative 6: Pay Close Attention to a System's Effect on People

Management will be not only helping itself but also going a long way to smoothing out employee misunderstanding by first naming a competent, tactful, resourceful supervisor for the new installation. It matters little if this person is hired from inside or outside the company, so long as he is chosen first for his ability to handle people, second for his understanding of business problems, and third for his technical aptitude. A supervisor meeting these qualifications will be of invaluable assistance in educating employees to the new system.

According to the experience of many companies, the surest way of allaying unnecessary fears among employees about the new system is to keep them fully and frankly informed from the moment the new system is being contemplated. When a firm decision has been made to convert to the new system, management must see that the new system is explained to employees in terms of their individual jobs and of management's over-all objectives. Meetings should be held to permit employees to ask questions about the projected system, to solicit their suggestions and help in planning, and to keep them informed during the course of planning.

Imperative 7: Plan Constantly for the Future

After a punched-card installation has been "shaken down" and is operating smoothly, management should, with the help of the supervisor, look toward the future. If the installation has been started at one point, then planning should be undertaken—*according to the original plans as determined by the profit objectives,* if possible—to extend it to other clerical operations. But this immediate planning should also be carried out with an awareness that newer, faster types of data processing equipment are in prospect. It is a good idea, consequently, to keep the methods study group intact so that it can monitor data processing developments. Here the supervisor can be of help in maintaining contact with equipment manufacturers and other firms.

The fact that a firm has made the conversion to punched cards makes the step to a more advanced method of data processing much shorter. It is most unlikely that the principles underlying the use of these newer methods will differ materially from those underlying the use of punched cards.

12

Punched Cards and the Future

Many businessmen are understandably skeptical of punched cards as the data processing method of the future. Bombarded as they are by news reports and magazine articles describing the wonderful business world of the future, responsible executives can well wonder if punched cards are not just one transitory step along the way to an ultimate, perfect clerical system. At any rate, the swelling volume of publicity heralding the wonderful new computers makes the average executive wonder if a punched-card installation won't be obsolete, if not next year, then five or ten years from now. What of the future of punched cards? The steady progress toward the development of machines that will handle business data without the need for first recording these data in punched-card form cannot be denied. But no one can deny, either, that *the principles governing data handling by these future electronic machines will be much the same as those governing punched-card methods today.* Thus, whether it be today or some distant tomorrow, management will have to grapple with these same principles when it converts to automatic data processing methods.

Will Punched Cards Become Obsolete?

To predict flatly that the punched card will remain with us indefinitely as a data processing medium would be presumptuous. Technical advances are coming so fast in the data processing field that

144

punched-card equipment might become obsolete sooner than expected. Even the manufacturers of punched-card equipment are not behaving as though they have a vested interest in perpetuating their equipment. They are bending every effort to develop machines and methods to help business improve its data processing. In the face of all this, therefore, punched cards would seem to stand in some peril of extermination. Thus, experts foresee them being displaced by other devices, such as original records containing data written in magnetic ink and able to be processed by machines having *character-recognition ability*. This data processing method is gaining acceptance in the banking business to speed up the handling of checks.

If an argument were to be put forward in support of punched-card methods, it would best be based on the unit-record principle. Because of this principle, punched cards stand a good chance of staying in use for some time. As embodied in punched cards, the unit-record principle is the most inexpensive answer to problems of data retrieval, processing of small quantities of data, fast sorting of data, etc. The fact that the unit-record principle is important on a larger scale explains also why manufacturers of electronic computers have provided card input and output for their larger units. Again, manufacturers have increased substantially the speed with which punched-card machines can manipulate, calculate, and print out data contained in cards. Just as a computer installation does not necessarily eliminate a firm's need for adding and bookkeeping machines, so in business generally the development of high-speed computers does not make punched-card installations obsolete.

Technology aside, the fact that a firm has converted to punched-card data processing does not mean that it has taken a hasty step in the wrong direction. The basic principles governing the handling of data by punched-card methods are the same principles governing data handling by more complex computer installations. Indeed, the firm that has installed punched-card equipment has won a good part of the battle when making the further change to a computer. The firm has already mastered the chief problems underlying the mass production handling of data; and its management and personnel are well aware of the demands that automatic data processing makes upon them.

In this sense, then, punched cards are emphatically not in danger of becoming obsolete. Rather they become a logical steppingstone to whatever methods and machines the future will impose.

Widening Applications for Punched Cards

Automatic data processing has, in a matter of years, ceased to be a mechanical or electronic curiosity and become a practical necessity in the average office. In the years coming, data processing methods employing the basic principles of punched-card systems will penetrate most business. Further, these various methods will undoubtedly become more compatible with each other so that data will flow from business to business in coded form without being converted to written or printed records. Just as automatic long-distance dialing now permits a telephone user to reach a party in another city without first talking to a succession of switchboard operators, so will the individual data processing installations of firms become linked with one another to transmit routine transaction data.

The most routine of such transactions involve the exchange of goods and services: buying and selling. Many of these transactions are wasteful, time-consuming, subject to delays, fraught with uncertainties, and not infrequently buried under excessive paperwork. Even now, in an attempt to eliminate the chaos surrounding the efforts of one firm to purchase merchandise from another, several smaller companies are using punched-card methods. Consider the following examples.

• A tool company affixes punched tags to packages of tool steel being shipped to distributors. As each distributor sells these packages out of his stock, he returns the tags to the manufacturer. These tags are automatically converted to punched cards, which are then used to (1) prepare a monthly inventory report for the distributor and (2) print out an invoice and shipping papers covering a replacement shipment of tool steel to restore the distributor's inventory. Thus, the purchase order that the distributor would normally prepare and mail to the manufacturer has been eliminated. In addition, both manufacturer and distributor are provided with accurate control over shipments and inventory.

• The purchasing department of an aircraft manufacturer duplicates item description cards covering expendable tools (grinding wheels, cutting tools, etc.) that it orders regularly in quantity from certain suppliers. These cards are sent to the suppliers, who run them through their own machines to print current price information for each item on each card. Each card has been keypunched in the suppliers' machine accounting department with the latest price information. The cards can then be destroyed and the printed price list returned to the aircraft manufacturer.

• A distributor is using part of the disk-memory capacity of a IBM Ramac 305 to keep track of cutting tool and abrasive inventories carried by his biggest customers in their own stockrooms. When the machine indicates (on the basis of periodic consumption quantities given the distributor by each customer) that certain stocks have reached an ordering point, it automatically prepares an invoice covering a new shipment to the customer. A customer is, therefore, spared the time and expense of maintaining his own stock control and writing purchase orders to replenish stocks.

Closing the Loop

As the list of punched-card applications is being extended every day as more firms explore new ways of lightening the paperwork load and improving their operating efficiency, a most significant development stands on the business horizon: the *automatic factory*. Punched cards, punched paper tape, and magnetic tape are being used to operate fabricating and processing machinery. Several steel rolling mills, for example, have been operated automatically with cards punched with codes that, when read, adjust the mill's speed and pressure for each pass of the hot billet. Many machine tools—turret drills, lathes, milling machines—are now operated by punched cards or punched paper tape. The chemical, oil, steel, and public utility industries are quickly moving in the direction of turning whole plant operations over to digital computers. Similar effort in other fields will soon bring forth the *automatic store* and *automatic warehouse*.

Much work is being done, particularly in connection with factory automation, on the closed-loop idea. This would bring a plant under such a degree of computer control that even the human task of reading regulating gauges and making the required adjustments in the machine or process would be assumed by the computer. But the closed-loop idea will not be confined to factory control. The systems being contemplated would be capable of automatically transmitting accounting, payroll, and inventory data back to the computer as various production steps are completed. And eventually, as a United States Steel

Corporation official informed *Business Week,* these business data will be automatically transmitted from the production control computer to the central data processing machine for a printout of various records and reports. Taking the idea further, it is not improbable that the input of customer order and sales forecast data will automatically activate the production units in the factory. The closed-loop idea will, therefore, encircle office and factory, creating an unbroken flow of data between the two.

The closed-loop idea might ultimately characterize transactions among a number of companies. It might well happen that a Denver distributor's computer, for example, would automatically transmit data indicating the approaching stockout of an item to the computer of a Chicago manufacturer and automatically initiate production or shipment operations at the plant. Accounting and other data generated by the transaction would be automatically processed at each point.

Questions of detail arise immediately as to the feasibility of this latter idea. Will the various automatic data processing and production control systems ever become sufficiently compatible with one another to make such automation possible? Will differing tax regulations, price arrangements, cost levels, and the countless exceptions found in every firm's transactions severely inhibit efforts to close such a far-ranging loop? No informed answer is possible. At least, however, the trend is unmistakable and of some consequence to the user of even a modest punched-card installation, because his installation might be playing a more decisive part in his firm's future than could be suspected at this early time.

New Directions for Management

The future possibilities of automatic data processing are eyed hopefully by some observers, apprehensively by others. Some see the definite possibility of automatic systems reaching the point of usurping many of management's most cherished prerogatives. They have forecast the decline and demise of certain management groups as a result of automatic data processing taking over many functions now performed by those groups. They contend that many members of middle management, for example, are engaged in making structured decisions, which could be adequately made by a computer. The weekly meeting of sales, production, and procurement people to determine a production schedule, for instance, involves the analysis of quantitative facts, which in many companies is now handled by automatic data processing.

But other observers prefer to view automatic data processing as capable of opening new opportunities to management, opportunities heretofore unrealized because of management's entanglement with time-consuming routine and detail. These observers doubt that automatic data processing will ever destroy the art of management:

> Changes will not proceed as fast or as far as some enthusiasts have been claiming. The new technology will change the *content* of many management jobs, particularly in the middle ranks where the structured types of decisions have tended to cluster. But the changes occurring over the next two decades will not erode or destroy the jobs. Instead, they will present opportunities for extending management capability and performance in areas which have often suffered from scant attention . . . the so-called unstructured areas in which questions of what to do and how to do it call for imagination and insight.[1]

The vista thus presented to management is both promising and startling. The prospect of being able to devote full attention to the control and planning of the business freed from the tedium of clerical detail, to make decisions on the basis of accurate and complete facts, and to have more time to assess the company's position vis-à-vis its customers and competition would gladden any executive. Nor should the vista be dimmed by mentioning the possibility that management might not succeed in applying automatic methods profitably; the preceding chapters have put sufficient stress on the great importance of management's full participation in planning and operating a system. The point is, rather, that ultimate success in a business world dominated by the new systems will make markedly new demands on management. These demands may be summed up in the warning of yet another observer: "Management will not only be released to think, it will be *forced* to think." And management will find its thinking proceeding in several new directions.

Emphasis on Management Training. Few influences have brought management closer to fundamentals than automatic data processing. Even the basic punched-card installation's handling of an elementary

---

[1] Melvin Ashen, "The Manager and the Black Box," *Harvard Business Review,* November–December, 1960, pp. 85–92.

sales analysis often teaches a manager more about his firm's products and markets than he could learn by other means. Conversely, the more procedures he wishes to commit to an automatic system, the more a manager must understand the fundamental business principles involved. As automatic systems are improved and made capable of handling more sophisticated procedures (operations research, for example), their profitable applications will require that management be trained in the new techniques. Moreover, many of the newer methods of training, such as decision-making games and simulation, which employ data processing units, will be extensively used.

Another consequence of automatic data processing necessitating training will be organizational changes. Most companies applying the new systems experience realignments in executive duties. In some cases, because there are complete reassignments of managers to new duties, more or less continuous training goes on.

Awareness of the Changing Market. No competent businessman ever ignores the demands of the market. But the introduction of new data processing methods makes the changing market the fast-changing market. The ability of these methods to provide quick, reliable market analyses and market forecasts will increase management's awareness of shifts occurring in tastes and trends. As a result, management will be obliged to spend more of its time in developing new products and services in obedience to these shifts.

Awareness of New Systems. As mentioned in previous chapters, the profitable application of a punched-card system does not conclude management's responsibilities toward new data processing ideas. It merely sets management on the right road. From that point on, it will have the responsibility of keeping well informed on new systems coming into use even in business situations far removed from its own. Thus, a closed-loop system installed in a power plant should be seriously considered for its future implications.

In practice, this awareness can be stimulated by setting up within the firm some means whereby new methods and ideas are heeded, assessed, and acted upon. Many firms give the manager of the machine accounting or data processing department the chance to attend conventions and trade shows to keep abreast of new developments. He is able to pass this information on to a receptive member of top management. It is of great importance that this search for ideas be made a matter of continuing policy. Subjecting the search to spasmodic whims of economy can not only deprive the firm of vital intelligence but also discourage the search itself.

These are but some of the new directions management will be taking in the years ahead. For very many firms, these years will be unmarked by spectacular or even drastic change but certainly remarkable for a widening use of automatic data processing by all manner of businesses. Accordingly, growth and survival will prompt many a firm to join the main stream of business development by installing punched-card or common-language units, or a computer, or even a modest photocopy unit—at any rate, taking some action to scale down the paperwork pyramid blocking its path to better management and sounder profits.

The Case Book — Part I

The two sections of the Case Book contain descriptions of actual punched-card applications. The first section, immediately following, covers installations using standard punched-card equipment. The second section (pages 195 to 222) deals with installation using computers having punched-card input and output.

The cases in both sections cover the use of punched-card data processing by a variety of businesses: manufacturing, wholesaling, banking, and the like. The clerical operations include order processing, billing, inventory control, production control, cost estimating, mortgage loan accounting, and payroll.

Although each case describes the application of punched-card methods to the specific requirements of a particular company, the reader should not conclude that it has no relevance to his own data processing needs. In the first place, certain applications, such as billing and inventory control, vary little in their essentials from one firm to another. In studying the cases, therefore, the reader should find one or more procedures pertinent to his own situation. Second, the cases have been chasen to reveal the versatility of punched-card methods, to illustrate that the unit-record idea is as applicable to an involved production control procedure as it is to a simple order processing routine. This should dispel the notion that punched cards are best used only for the least complex procedures.

Each of the applications described in both sections of the Case Book required the establishment of objectives, painstaking analysis of the firm's data processing needs, and the careful planning of a punched-card installation to satisfy these needs. Significantly, top management

152

in each case took an active part in planning the installation, and one or more of its members were in direct charge of setting up the system and overseeing the operation of the final installation.

To assist the reader, the various operational steps are numbered to correspond with numbers on the flow charts accompanying each case.

1-1. A BASIC PUNCHED-CARD INSTALLATION

Bozzuto's, Inc., Waterbury, Connecticut, is a grocery wholesaler and distributor with annual sales of $6 million. Employing 45 persons, the firm supplies about 325 accounts. It bills 1,200 invoices a week; with the average order running about sixty lines, the firm bills over 14,000 lines daily.

Installation (IBM): Printing card punch, sorter, 402 accounting machine, reproducing punch, summary punch.

General Procedure. Bozzuto's uses a basic punched-card installation: card punch, sorter, and accounting machine or tabulator. These units handle the basic processing steps of recording, classifying, and summarizing the data. The reproducing punch serves mainly to ease the manipulation of the 100,000 cards consumed monthly. No calculating punch is required, since the billing operation requires only totaling of single-unit cards by the tabulator.

Two kinds of master cards are kept in tub files: item masters and customer masters. For each customer, there are three masters: name card, street address card, and city card, thereby giving a three-line name and address on the printed invoice. Since there are four price categories used by Bozzuto's, the appropriate price category for each customer is coded and punched into the name card.

The item master card is keypunched when merchandise arrives at the company's warehouse. This card contains both printed and punched data on description, code number, cost and selling prices, and size and number of units per selling quantity. The item master is kept on file as long as that particular item is stocked; when there is a change in basic information, the card is destroyed and a new card is punched. The item master is used to gang-punch item cards for each case, bundle, package, or other selling unit. These single-unit cards, held in the tub file, represent the actual number of items in the warehouse; thus, for 100 packages of an item, 100 cards would be gang-punched from the matching item master.

In the case of large quantities of an item, a running summary of stock position is kept on a separate card, and additional cards for in-stock items are punched as needed. This prevents the tub file from becoming jammed with too many cards. This summary card also carries a notation showing at what point an item should be reordered. When an item is reordered, the date is written on the summary card and the date the merchandise is received is also marked down.

Order Entry and Billing. Orders are received from four sources: outside salesman, in the mail from stores, telephoned orders, and "window calls" (customers ordering at the warehouse). The bulk of the orders are received from Bozzuto's salesmen.

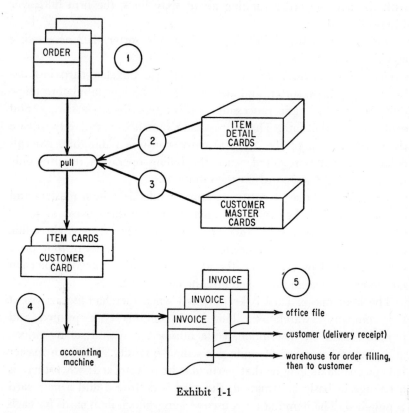

Exhibit 1-1

1. As orders are received, they are arranged in reverse delivery order. This means that, when the orders are eventually filled in the warehouse, the first items loaded on the truck will be the last off the truck. Each order is, therefore, immediately ready for delivery at the

customer's door. Each order is also *sequence numbered* in the warehouse, so that all items on the same order carry the same number. This eliminates errors due to omitting items at a dropoff.

2. After the orders have been put in delivery sequence, the appropriate item cards are pulled from the tub file. The cards are filed alphabetically by product groups; i.e., all vegetables in one section, all fruits in another, and so on.

3. When all item cards have been pulled, the customer master, or "header," cards are added to each set.

4. The order deck of punched cards is then processed through the accounting machine, producing a three-part printed invoice. The accounting machine totals, for each order, like item cards, thus printing only one line for each item. For example, if there are 10 cards for 10 units of an item ordered by the customer, the tabulator prints out a one-line description and the various totals that it has accumulated: total quantity, selling price, cost price, and taxable items. The tabulator then adds up these subtotals to print the total invoice amount.

5. One copy of the invoice is kept on file in the office. This copy contains cost information used in cost accounting. The same data appears on customer copies on a perforated strip, which is removed before the invoice leaves the office.

The invoice itself is used by the warehouse to fill the order. The remaining two copies of the invoice go along with the order. One copy is used as a delivery receipt, the customer signing for the items received, and is returned to the office by the truck driver. The third copy is the customer's file copy, on which he remits within seven days. No statements are issued by Bozzuto's. Most collections are made by the salesmen for the merchandise delivered the previous week.

Accounts Receivable. This procedure includes the following steps:

6. When the delivery receipt copy of the invoice is returned to the office, it is checked against the office copy for possible changes. A summary card containing constant customer and product data is punched automatically for each order by a summary punch as the invoice is printed. New data include invoice number, date, and amount.

7. These summary cards are filed as an open-item accounts receivable file and are used at the end of the week to print an accounts receivable register on the tabulator. Entries on the register are listed in invoice number sequence. The cards are then sorted and filed in customer sequence.

8. When payments are received, the matching summary cards are pulled, the ledger posted, and the accounts receivable register reconciled. Summary cards for paid orders are destroyed.

Results. Between 1947 and 1959, Bozzuto's sales volume grew twelvefold, and yet it is still using the same punched-card installation decided on in 1947. As a result, the firm's payroll has increased only 4½ times—"with the majority of our people in sales, delivery, and warehouse work," remarks President Adam Bozzuto. "We estimate it would take three times our present office force to handle our volume if we were still using our former methods."

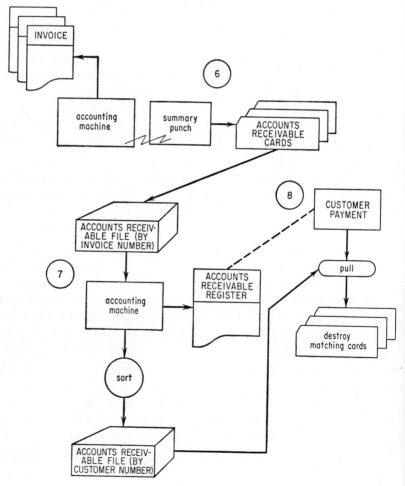

Exhibit 1-2

The punched-card system has also encouraged customers' confidence in the firm, according to Bozzuto. "A printed, machine-produced invoice tells a customer that the chance of human error in calculations, transcribing, and order-filling has been reduced to a minimum. We have on record several instances of new business coming to us because the retailer knew we used modern machine accounting methods."

1-2. A LOW-COST INSTALLATION

Hampden-Harvard Breweries, Inc., Willimansett, Massachusetts, produces beer under several brand names, which is trucked daily to about 250 wholesale customers in the Northeastern states.

Installation (Remington Rand): Card punch, sorter, interpreter, reproducing punch, tabulator, summary punch.

The original Hampden Brewery was long known as one of the oldest ale producers, but following World War II, in response to public preference, management decided to switch production to beer. By 1953, beer production equaled that of ale for the first time and by the following year had surpassed it. By 1959, Hampden-Harvard was involved in the first stages of a $5 million expansion program to keep abreast of beer demand.

This growth revealed the inadequacy of the firm's manual methods of billing, routing, and preparing sales reports. "We were getting sales reports three to four weeks too late to be of any use," says President Harold M. Broderick. "The very growth that we had encouraged threatened us with chaos because of outmoded data handling methods."

Problems showed up in four areas: (1) production scheduling was a matter mostly of educated guesswork; (2) an increase or decrease in sales did not show up until it was too late to do anything about it; (3) order processing was slow, resulting in split shipments and, consequently, higher transportation costs; and (4) since all figure entries were made manually, errors were common and customer complaints inevitable.

A punched-card system was installed in 1958, and at the present time it handles billing, invoicing, accounts receivable, shipping instructions, routing, and sales analysis reports.

The Procedures. The following is a general description of the order processing, billing, and related procedures (paragraph numbers correspond to those on the accompanying flow charts):

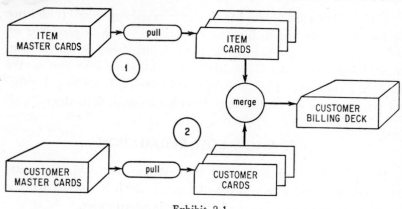

Exhibit 2-1

1. Prepunched item cards (one card for each case of beer) are filed in a tub file by state brand. According to quantities shown on each customer's and salesman's order, the required number of cards is pulled. The reproducer punches new cards periodically to recharge this file.

2. Customer cards pulled from a master customer-card file are reproduced and merged with item cards to create a customer billing deck.

3. The various billing decks are sorted by geographical areas of

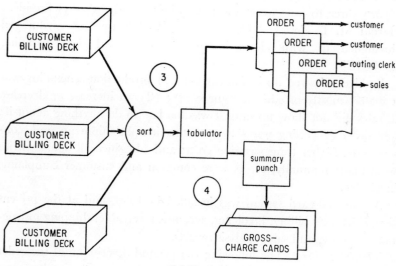

Exhibit 2-2

customers and run through the tabulator, which prints out the day's orders in quadruplicate. One copy of the order goes to the sales department, another to the routing clerk who combines the various orders by truck and route, and the last two copies are given to the drivers. One of these is the customer's copy, and the other is returned with the number of empty bottles noted on it.

4. As the orders are printed by the tabulator, a summary punch automatically creates a summary, or gross-charge, card for each customer. These cards are held in a suspense file.

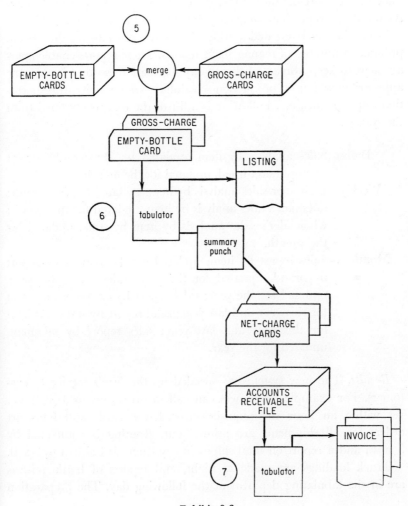

Exhibit 2-3

5. From a tub file of prepunched item cards for empty bottles, clerks pull the proper number of cards indicated on returned copies of orders and match them with gross-charge cards in the suspense file.

6. The combined deck of cards is run through the tabulator to obtain a listing. At the same time, the summary punch creates net-charge cards, which are kept in an accounts receivable file.

7. At the end of the month, the net-charge cards are run through the tabulator to obtain invoices for each customer. There are approximately five thousand separate orders that must be included in these invoices. At the same time, the cards are sorted and run through the tabulator to produce an aged trial balance of receivables.

From the cards created during the above procedures, the system produces a number of management reports. These reports enable management to keep abreast of day-to-day fluctuations so that it can take appropriate action on production scheduling, sales activity, transportation requirements, etc. Following is a list of the reports obtained from the system:

Daily: Sales analysis by item, updated for the month; report of empties returned, updated for the month.

Weekly: Customer sales analysis by item, updated for the month; salesman's sales analysis by item, updated for the month; wholesaler's sales analysis by item by state, updated for the month.

Monthly: Sales report by item, updated for the year; sales report by brand, updated for the year; sales report by state, updated for the year; sales report by customer and item for this year and last year; sales report by state and item for this year and last year; sales report by salesman, updated for the year.

Results. The new system has speeded up the firm's service to customers. For example, customers can call in orders up to 3:30 P.M.; yet within an hour the requisite gross-charge cards and four-part orders for all shipments are printed out. Routing is completed by 5 P.M., and a report on total shipments by trucks is finished by 5:30.

Truck loadings are made at night, and reports of bottle returns are in the tabulating department the following day. The preparation of net-charge cards for accounts receivable purposes is completed before noon of the same day. This leaves machine time available for the preparation of the various management reports.

The company plans to continue expanding its facilities and feels that the punched-card system can be expanded with it. It is anticipating converting payroll, general ledger, and general inventory control to the system.

"We have learned," says Broderick, "that as we grow we must maintain parallel growth in paperwork procedures, or risk forfeiting the advantages that growth might have for us."

1-3. PUNCHED CARDS AND AUTOMOTIVE WHOLESALING

Boston Motor Parts Company, Inc., Boston, is a wholesaler of automotive parts, serving dealers, general garages, and fleet owners. The firm stocks 20,000 different parts.

Installation (Remington Rand): Two Card-O-Matic card punches, printing multiplying punch (calculating punch), sorter, interpreter, tabulator. (The Card-O-Matic punch enables an operator to reproduce data automatically from prepunched master cards into new detail cards and to punch variable data manually into the same cards.)

Order Processing and Invoicing. Dealers served by the firm are furnished with special order forms on which they record automotive parts disbursements from their stock. These forms are sent daily to Boston Motor Parts, which accumulates them for a week and then ships replacement stock to each dealer. A normal thirty days' usage is established by each dealer as an ideal inventory level for each part. Thus, by placing an order with the wholesaler every day for parts used that day, the dealer receives once a week sufficient stock to maintain his inventory at a working minimum.

This is the procedure followed once orders have been received from dealers and also from general garages and fleet owners (the latter two using their own order forms). The paragraph numbers correspond to those on the accompanying flow charts.

1. The orders are edited, and classified according to the discount applying to each of the three types of customers.

2. Card-punch operators pull part master cards for items appearing on each order. Automatically, the punch reproduces constant data

from each master card (part catalogue number, alphabetical description, storage location in warehouse, unit price, and a classification indicating supplier of part) into a new detail card. Manually, the operator punches variable data into each detail card (customer code, shipping date, order number, type-of-customer code, quantity of item).

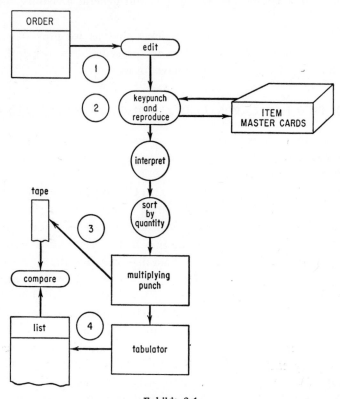

Exhibit 3-1

These cards are run through the interpreter, which prints identifying data across the top of each card.

3. The cards are sorted by quantity for group multiplication in a printing multiplying punch. Each quantity group is multiplied by the unit price, and the extension is punched automatically into each card. The multiplying punch produces a tape showing the extensions.

4. The cards are run through the tabulator to obtain a list showing totals by quantity groups. These totals can be compared with those appearing on the multiplying punch's tape.

5. The cards are sorted by type of customer and classification of parts. Prepunched master cards with the correct discounts for the various combinations of classes are merged with the detail cards, and the whole deck is run through the multiplying punch. The punch applies the correct discount to each detail card and punches into it the net charge for each part.

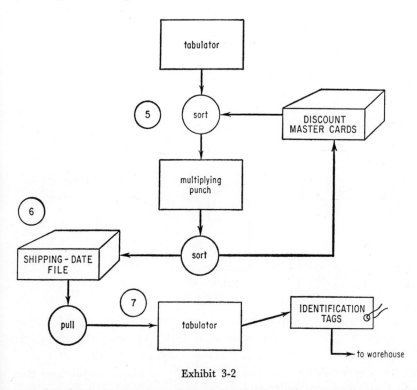

Exhibit 3-2

6. The cards are sorted by shipping date and held in a file.

7. On the day prior to shipment, all cards filed for that day are sorted by customer and also by the sequence in which the ordered parts are stored in the warehouse. These cards are run through the tabulator, which prints an identification tag for each group of similar items ordered by a customer.

The shipping tags are sent to the warehouse for picking the items. Because the tags are arranged in storage location sequence, there is no backtracking to fill an order. As each part or group of parts is pulled from the bins, the tag is attached, thus identifying it during shipping. The tags also ease the dealer's job of storing parts in his stock room.

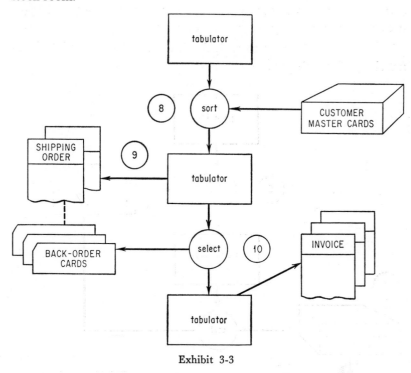

Exhibit 3-3

8. After the tags have been printed, the cards are sorted by part number and by the classification of parts. These cards are merged with customer master cards pulled manually from the file.

9. The whole deck is run through the tabulator to produce two-part shipping orders. One copy of the shipping order accompanies each shipment; the originals are retained in the office.

On the morning after shipment, the shipping order copies are used to pull manually the cards representing items that must be back-ordered. These cards are placed in a back-order file. The customer has already been advised of back-ordered items, because he has received the matching identification tags attached to his copy of the shipping order.

10. After the back-order cards have been selected from the deck, the remainder of the cards are run through the tabulator to print in-

voices. The tabulator accumulates and prints a total for each group of parts and also a grand total for each invoice.

Back Orders. Each week, the back-order cards (see step 9, above) are sorted by part number, and a report is prepared on the tabulator showing the total quantity of each part back ordered. This report goes to the buyer, who is thus able to study those parts for which inadequate stock has been maintained.

Inventory Control. At the end of each week, all item detail cards representing sales are sorted by part number. These cards are listed on the tabulator, and the list is sent to the inventory control record, where the week's disbursements are posted. A new balance on hand is written.

The inventory control record is reviewed periodically by buyers to check the inventory operating level established for each item. By this method, a check is made on those parts for which requirements have lessened, indicating that the inventory level should be lowered. When this is determined, the master part card involved is repunched showing a zero as a prefix to the classification code. Thereafter, such an item is segregated and is not ordered from the parts plant until stock has been reduced to the new level.

At the same time, a new master card is punched without a zero code, so that the regular order processing procedure can be carried out.

Purchasing. The item detail cards representing sales are used to print weekly purchase orders, which are sent to Boston Motor Parts' chief supplier, the Chrysler plant. Cards representing items not manufactured by this plant (as indicated by the part classification code) are, of course, sorted out. Each purchase order is reviewed by the buyer before being released.

Those parts identified in their respective cards by a zero code are not reordered until their stock level is down to the new minimum. Thus, the purchasing procedure is in step with the firm's sales volume.

A copy of the purchase order is sent to the receiving department to be used in checking in parts when they are delivered from the parts plant. The Chrysler packing slip can be checked against the order, since all items are in the same sequence. Further, the warehouse location sequence is shown on the purchase order copy (it appeared as constant data in the part master card) for each part, thereby speeding up storage.

Results. The punched-card installation has netted Boston Motor Parts several beneficial results:

1. Although the firm has tripled its business since the system was installed, it has added only three clerks in the office.

2. The buyers now devote their time only to exceptions; routine purchase orders are processed automatically.

3. Because all part data are contained in one master card file, price changes can be made quickly and accurately. The card-punch operator is able to reproduce the constant data automatically and to keypunch the new prices manually in a new card.

4. Inventory has been brought into closer balance with sales.

5. Warehouse, shipping, and receiving operations have been speeded up.

6. Service to customers has been improved, and a basis has been laid for better management control through analyses of transactions.

1-4. PUNCHED CARDS AND PAYROLL

Marquette Division, Curtiss-Wright Corporation, Cleveland, manufactures precision parts and assemblies, including standard-line products and items to customer specifications. Among the standard products produced are hydraulic governors for diesel and gasoline engines, precision spring clutches, electric and hydraulic windshield wipers for aircraft, a power steering system for boats, and the Swench impact wrench.

Installation (IBM): Two card punches, two verifiers, collator, two sorters, two 402 accounting machines, document-originating machine, alphabetical interpreter, calculating punch.

Need for Punched Cards. As an independent company, Marquette had for years been paying employees in cash, using a pay stub for record purposes. Pay was computed by extending information obtained from a clock card and a labor-distribution sheet for each employee. With only about 450 shop personnel and an office force of some 150, this system was considered adequate.

When the company became part of a large corporation, it was faced with new closing dates, new systems, and new report requirements. "Our previous system was not sufficiently flexible," says Marquette's general manager, W. E. MacEwen, "to take on the added requirements. It was necessary to change procedures to become fully integrated into the Curtiss-Wright organization." The result was the change-over to punched cards.

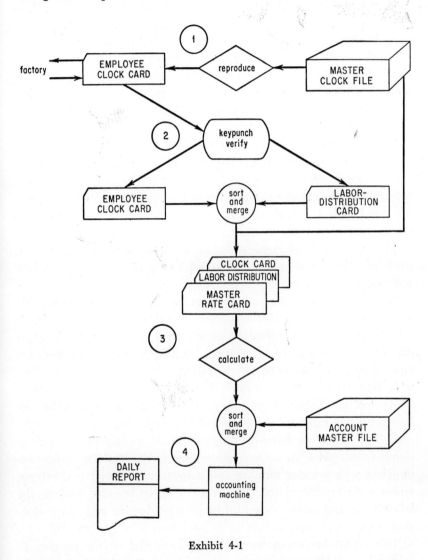

Exhibit 4-1

Payroll Procedure. Punched-card processing of Marquette's payroll falls into two phases: daily and weekly. Below is a step-by-step description of both phases (paragraph numbers correspond to those on the accompanying flow charts):

1. Daily clock cards are reproduced on a document-originating machine (reproducing punch) from a master clock or rate file. Each master card is prepunched with constant data on clock number, shift, plant number, rate of pay, type of labor, and employee name.

As it punches the daily clock cards, the document-originating machine also end-prints each card with plant number, department number, clock number, shift, and date. Other punched data are printed on the face of each card by an alphabetical interpreter.

The cards are sent to the factory and distributed in racks beside each time clock.

After an employee rings in at the time clock, he keeps his clock card with him throughout the day. It is his responsibility to enter the appropriate information on the card for each job he performs: time for each job, job number, type of task, account number charged with job, total daily hours, department charged, standard hours, and total pieces made. Timekeepers assist men in entering proper information.

After the employee rings out of his home department, his and the cards of other employees are collected and approved by the various foremen in charge.

2. In the machine accounting department, the clock cards are first sorted and matched with the master clock file to make sure none is missing. Card-punch operators punch total hours into daily clock cards and punch a labor-distribution detail card for each job operation entered by the employee on the clock card.

3. By merging the master clock file with the labor-distribution detail cards and processing them through the calculating punch, the cost for each job is extended and punched into the labor-distribution cards.

4. The detail, or labor-distribution, cards are sorted on account number, merged with an account master file (containing cards prepunched with account number and name), run through a tabulator, and a daily report printed. This report lists, by account number, the labor hours and money expended by both production and nonproduction employees.

This report keeps management fully informed on the progress of each job with respect to labor costs. It forms an integral part of the work-in-progress inventory, which is composed of several other inputs. This inventory, although only indirectly connected with the actual payroll procedure, illustrates the interconnecting aspects of an over-all accounting system.

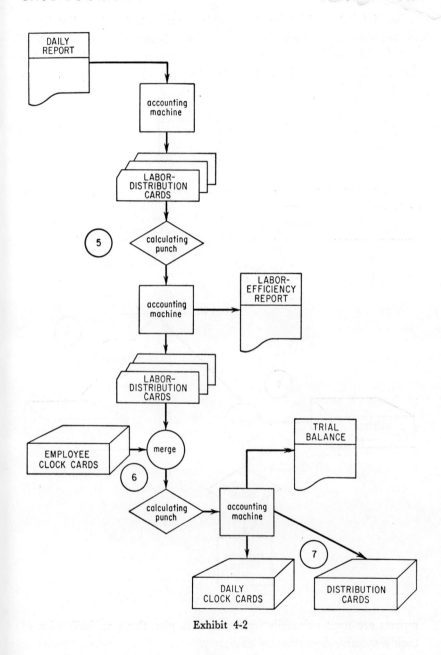

Exhibit 4-2

5. The calculating punch calculates and punches into the labor-distribution cards the percentage variance between actual hours and standard hours for each job. The cards are run through the accounting machine to obtain a daily direct-labor efficiency report. These

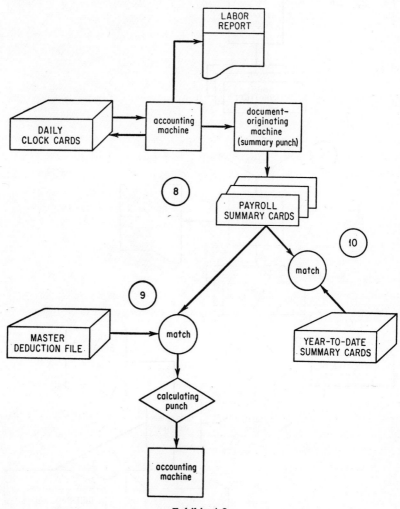

Exhibit 4-3

reports are used primarily by foremen to give them an indication of their respective departments' efficiency.

6. The employee daily clock cards are picked up again, merged with the labor-distribution cards, and put through the calculating

punch, which calculates and punches into the clock cards total money amounts for regular and premium hours plus night-shift differential, if any. The daily clock card now represents the employee's gross pay for the day. A trial balance is printed by the accounting machine, matching the total regular hours shown in the detail (labor-distribution) cards against those in the daily clock cards.

7. The labor-distribution cards are filed, and the daily clock cards (containing everything except deductions and net pay) are held in a file pending preparation of the weekly payroll.

Preparation of the weekly payroll is carried out by clock number sequence:

8. The accumulated daily clock cards for the week (step 7, above) are used to create a weekly labor report and a weekly payroll summary card for each employee. This is accomplished by hooking the document-originating machine into the tabulator to serve as a summary punch.

9. The summary cards are matched with a current deduction card and net earnings are calculated on the calculating punch and recorded in the summary card.

10. The summary cards have been merged and checked against the previous year-to-date file. When an employee's earnings reach the annual limit for FOAB deductions, the year-to-date card is punched to prevent any further deductions for the rest of the year. The current pay card is similarly punched, preventing the calculating punch from calculating the tax automatically.

11. Processing the completed summary cards and deduction cards through the accounting machine yields (1) payroll deduction register, (2) payroll check register, and (3) pay checks. Both hourly and salaried payroll can be thus processed; this is accomplished by substituting "retirement fund" for "union dues" on the salaried employees' checks. All other information is the same.

12. After the checks have been run off, the pay summary cards are matched with the previous year-to-date cards. The two sets of cards are run through the accounting machine to obtain a new year-to-date report and new year-to-date cards.

This completes the payroll cycle for the week.

Results. The system described above enables Marquette to meet reporting times and closing dates established by the parent Curtiss-Wright organization. All data for payroll, labor-distribution, and

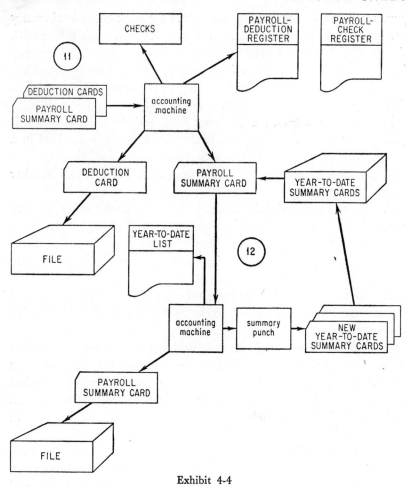

Exhibit 4-4

other accounting procedures derive from one card: the daily employee clock card. The entire weekly payroll is now completed three days sooner than was possible with former methods. Finally, considerable statistical information is now being obtained as a by-product of the payroll procedure.

1-5. JOB COSTS AND PUNCHED CARDS

Greenfield Tap & Die Corporation, Greenfield, Massachusetts, manufactures precision cutting tools: taps, dies, gauges, drills, reamers. The firm employs 1,200 persons.

Installation (Remington Rand): Thirteen card punches, six Card-O-Matic units, four tabulators, four sorters, two summary punches, Univac 60 calculating punch.

Because of the rigid technical standards required in the toolmaking industry and the high labor and material costs involved, errors in estimating costs can create a serious problem. Errors in manufacturing, whether caused by raw materials, equipment, or the human factor, must be detected promptly so that corrective action can be taken.

Although Greenfield uses its punched-card installation for payroll and sales and cost of sales analyses, this case is confined to a description of the procedure employed in determining the variance between actual and standard costs for each order.

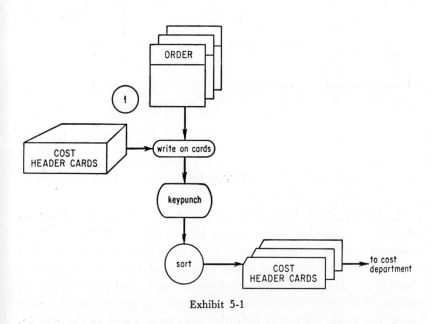

Exhibit 5-1

Job-cost Procedure. Two types of orders set production in motion: (1) customers' orders for standard or special items and (2) production orders prepared from a sales forecast for stock items. The cost procedure begins as production orders are released to the factory (paragraph numbers correspond to those appearing on accompanying flow charts):

1. Cost header cards are sent to the tabulating department. Written on these cards are descriptions and quantity of each item ordered,

dates, order number, and other indicative data. These data are punched in the card manually and verified. The cards are sorted by order number and routed to the cost department.

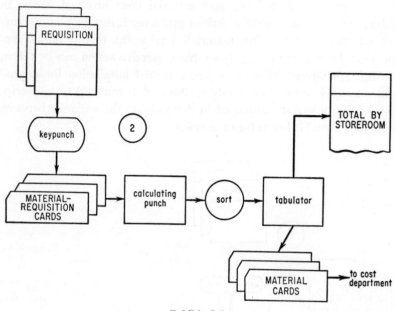

Exhibit 5-2

2. As material is issued from the stock room for each order, issue details are recorded manually on a material requisition card accompanying the order papers. The tabulating department punches and verifies these data and extends the material cost on the calculating punch. These cards are sorted by storeroom and run through the tabulator to obtain a subtotal by storeroom and a grand total for the day. The cards are sorted by order number and sent to the cost department.

3. As each operation is completed on an order, a job ticket is stamped in the timekeeper's office with the employee's name and number and also with the starting and finishing times for the operation. Each card has been previously hectographed with the order number, quantity, description, department, operation number and name, piecework allowances, and rate per hundred pieces.

In the tabulating department, these data are punched into each

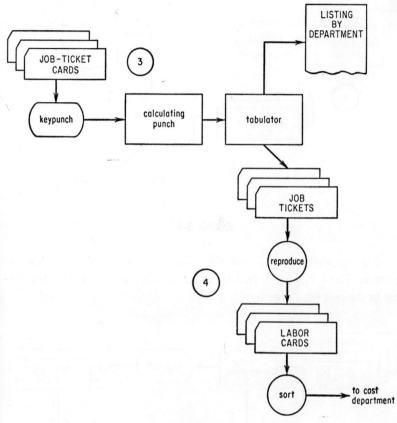

Exhibit 5-3

card and verified, extended for the labor amount, interpreted, and run through the tabulator for a listing by department.

4. The job ticket cards are reproduced, and a set of labor cards is produced. These cards are interpreted and sorted by order number and sent to the cost department. The job ticket cards are filed to produce the payroll at the close of the payroll period.

5. On completion of final inspection of an order, stock-movement sheets and stock-movement cards are sent to the tabulating department. The stock-movement sheets, made out by the inspection department, are priced and extended for standard cost by the payroll department. These data are punched in the stock-movement cards by the tabulating department. The cards are verified, interpreted, and extended by the calculating punch. They are sorted by product and

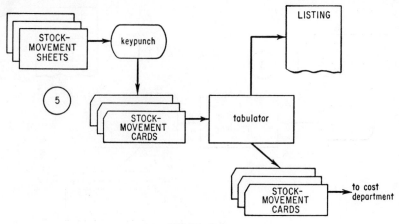

Exhibit 5-4

stock room and run through the tabulator for a listing in that sequence. The cards are sorted by order number and sent with the listing to the cost department.

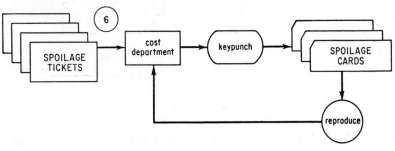

Exhibit 5-5

6. The inspection department makes out spoilage tickets, which are sent to the cost department for pricing and extending. The tabulating department punches spoilage cards from these tickets. The cards are reproduced and the duplicate set interpreted, sorted by order number, and sent to the cost department.

7. The cost department ascertains that all cards are filed for each order; that is, header cards, material cards, labor cards for each operation, spoilage cards, and stock-movement cards. When these cards have been checked, they are sent back to the tabulating department. They are sorted by labor class and by labor amount. Using a

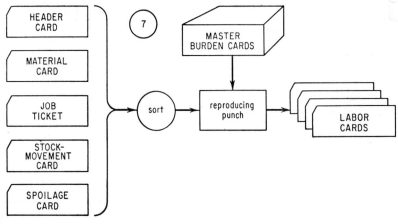

Exhibit 5-6

set of master burden cards, comparing on labor amount, the reproducer punches the burden and the total cost into the labor cards.

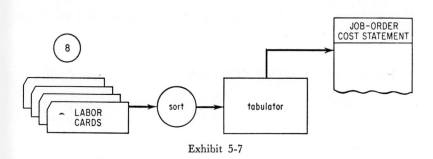

Exhibit 5-7

8. The labor cards are sorted by operation sequence number and
then by order number and are run through the tabulator to obtain
a job order cost statement for each order. The tabulator totals progressively all operations with labor and burden to the total cost. The
stock-movement card has the standard cost punched in the amount
field and has a credit-control hole punched. The spoilage is also
totaled as a credit.

The progressive grand total at the foot of the total cost column on
the job order cost sheet is the amount of variance beween the actual
and standard cost of the order.

Results. As a by-product of the job order cost routine, many subsequent tabulations are made from the same cards to provide management with effective control reports:

• Punched-card labor tickets are the basis for preparing the piecework payroll. Cards are punched for each rework job and are tabulated to show the foremen inefficiencies in their departments' operations. Similarly, spoilage cards are tabulated to exercise control over scrap.

• Many detailed analyses are made at the request of management reporting material usage, measured day work, production movement, and stock movement on shipments. These reports are prepared quickly and accurately, enabling management to start corrective measures while an order is in production.

• The costs of completed jobs are computed daily, immediately on completion of an order, to show the variance between actual and standard costs. This is an effective means of checking errors and inefficiencies.

• The completely mechanized payroll is prepared for 1,200 employees in two days. Payroll and personnel statistics are tabulated readily for any analysis.

1-6. MANUFACTURING CONTROL WITH PUNCHED CARDS

Sciaky Brothers, Inc., Chicago, manufactures resistance, brazing, and fusion-welding equipment, much of it used in the production of automative and military items. The firm employs 400 persons.

Installation (IBM): Three card punches, verifier, two sorters, collator, reproducing punch, interpreter, calculating punch, 407 accounting machine.

Since Sciaky's production consists almost entirely in manufacturing to customers' specifications, close controls over all phases of manufacture are needed. The firm's punched-card installation permits each production step to be monitored and at the same time yields reports containing current statistics on inventory, labor distribution and efficiency, sales, and engineering.

The basis of the system is the creation of a punched card representing each of the major manufacturing factors: money, materials, machines, labor, and movement through the plant. With each production step and machine component reflected in a punched card, management is able to follow the manufacturing process, evaluate it at any time, and correct or adjust it when necessary.

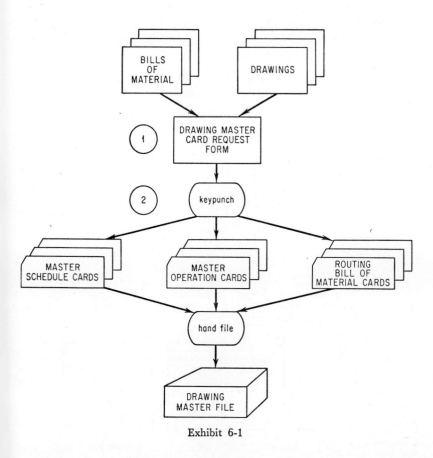

Exhibit 6-1

Production Control Procedure. There are two phases to Sciaky's production control as carried out with punched cards: (1) the preparatory phase of punching the necessary cards and (2) the movement of the cards through the factory during the manufacturing process. In the procedure description below, the paragraph numbers correspond to those on the accompanying flow charts.

1. When a piece of equipment is to be manufactured, a process engineer prepares a drawing master card request form. For each drawing shown in the bill of material of the part to be made, he itemizes which of the approximately eighty operation centers will

perform the work, the sequence of operations, the estimated setup, layout, and running times for each operation, and the tools or jigs that are to be used.

2. All these data are punched into schedule cards and operation cards. Also punched is a routing bill-of-material card, in which are indicated all the drawing numbers of the parts to be made for each bill of material or subassembly. Held in file, these cards give flexibility throughout the system; any drawing revisions made by the engineering department can be reflected in this master deck simply by punching new cards.

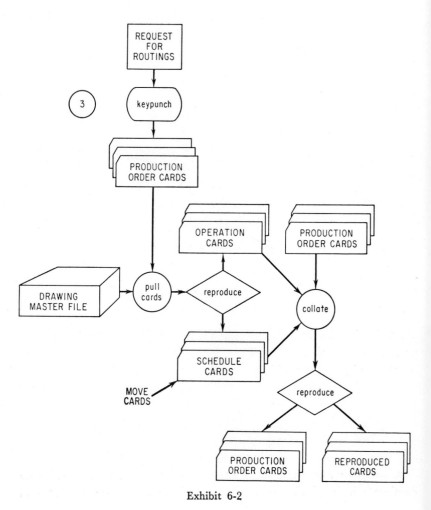

Exhibit 6-2

3. When an order is released, the production control department requests preparation of a production order master card. It contains manufacturing order number, bill-of-materials number, and number of units to be manufactured. These are used to pull the proper drawing master deck cards from the previously created file. From existing cards, move cards and operation cards are reproduced. These are punched with the total number of pieces to be made and the total time required for each operation.

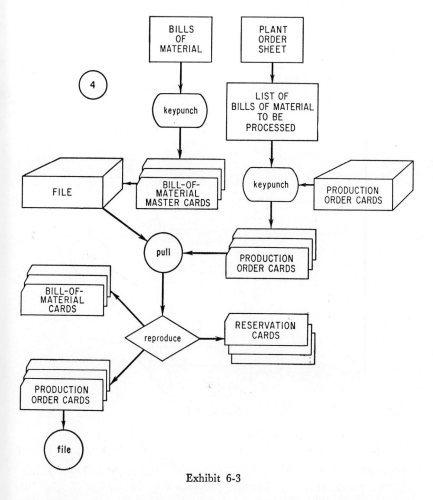

Exhibit 6-3

4. While the production control department is processing these cards for the labor to be performed, the material control section is in

action in another direction. It prepares forms from which a bill-of-materials master deck of cards is punched. These are used to create reservation cards for materials required from stores. Further machine processing creates purchase cards for parts not carried in standard stock. Run through the accounting machine, they produce a listing so that purchasing does not have to wait until the inventory control file has been analyzed before it starts procedures to obtain special items.

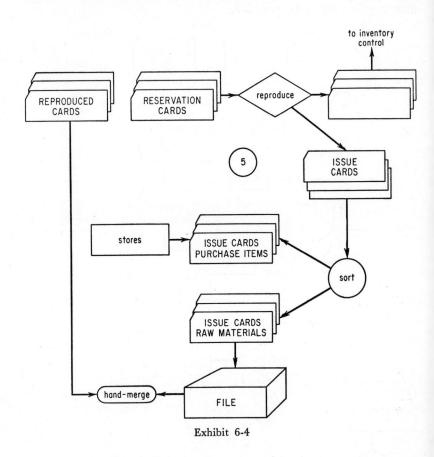

Exhibit 6-4

5. Issue cards, created from the reservation cards, are divided into two groups: cards calling for raw materials to be processed through the plant and cards representing purchased or stock items to be issued for assembly. The first type of cards is set aside in a pending file awaiting routine instructions, and the second type is sent to the stores

department with bills of material to be used in issuing parts to the assembly department on the proper date.

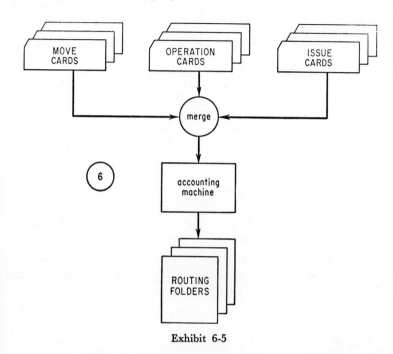

Exhibit 6-5

6. Move cards, operation cards, and material issue cards come together for a key step in the manufacturing control process. This involves processing the merged deck through the accounting machine to print specially designed *routing folders*. These manila folders are printed with a complete listing of information about the part to be manufactured and subsequently will be used to carry pertinent cards, reports, drawings, and (when feasible) even small parts from operation center to operation center through the manufacturing process.

7. The routing folder and all the documents that have been prepared go to the production control department where starting dates are scheduled. The dates are noted on a schedule report (printed on the accounting machine during step 6 above from the move cards), and this report is held in a binder for reference and control. The remainder of the documents and cards are handled as follows:

a. Operation cards and one set of schedule cards are placed in a pending file until three weeks before the starting date.

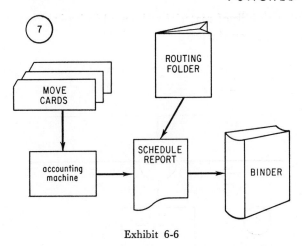

Exhibit 6-6

b. The routing folder is sent to the issuing department. It contains issue cards, move cards, labor cards, drawings, and tool and instruction sheets pertaining to the part being made.

c. A second set of schedule cards is filed in a production control work-in-process file by order and drawing number.

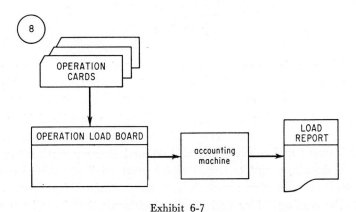

Exhibit 6-7

8. A second set of operation cards is filed in the production control machine-load file by operation center, individual machine number, and starting date. The machine-load file enables any changes to be made in scheduling simply by punching new cards. The work load for any individual operation centers can be reviewed at any time.

Each week all operation cards are removed from the file and run

through the accounting machine to prepare a load report by operation center or individual machine. This report totals the daily hours
planned for each center during the forthcoming weekly period. The
report compares the capacity total of each center. On this basis, management is able to determine if any subcontracting, rescheduling, or
overtime is required because of overloads. The operation cards are
refiled in the master machine-load file following completion of the
report.

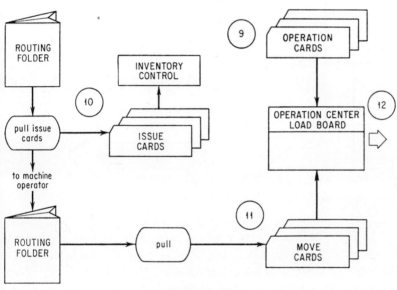

Exhibit 6-8

9. Processing of the order starts in the shop three weeks before the
beginning of the first machine operation. There is a visual load board
at each operation center in the factory. A production control clerk files
operation cards in each center.

10. The issuing department, meanwhile, has cut and issued the
material indicated on the routing folder for the operation that is about
to begin. The issue card is removed from the folder, compared with
the inventory item to make sure there is no discrepancy, and sent to
inventory control as notice that the material has been issued.

11. The routing folder and material necessary for manufacturing
the part are delivered to the starting operation center. The move card
is taken from the folder and filed in the load board in front of the

corresponding operation card. This serves as notice to the foreman that the material is in the department and can be scheduled to a machine at any time.

12. The foreman assigns work by removing the move and operation cards from the load board and placing them on a rack at the individual machine which will do the work. The routing folder and material are moved to the machine with the necessary tooling for the job.

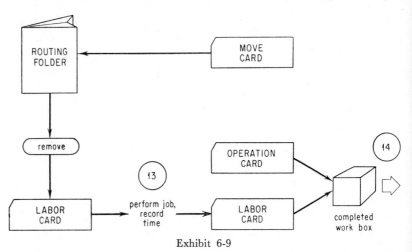

Exhibit 6-9

13. The machine operator uses a time clock to punch setup and running times into the labor card he takes from the routing folder. On this card he writes also his badge number, pieces finished, and operational machine number. When he completes the job, he places this card and the operation card in a completed-work box. An inspector or foreman takes the move card from the machine, inspects the parts, and replaces the move card in the routing folder. On the folder, the operation just completed is stamped with the date.

The routing folder then accompanies the material to the next operation center.

14. The labor and operation cards are picked up hourly from the completed-work boxes. A timekeeper extends the time punched in the labor cards and checks it against the standard time shown in the operation card. Any discrepancies are referred at once to the foreman. This hour-by-hour check enables production bottlenecks to be dealt with while the facts are fresh in everyone's mind. The reason for the delay is written on the back of the operation card.

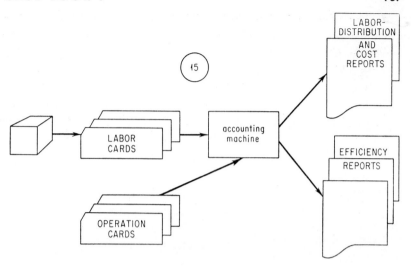

Exhibit 6-10

15. On the following morning, the labor cards are used to print labor-distribution reports and costs records. The operation cards are used to unload the master machine-load file in the production control department so that it does not reflect work already completed. The operation cards are then used in the preparation of reports showing operation center efficiency, employee efficiency, and comparison of standard and estimated hours by operation and by type of equipment manufactured.

Results. Through the application of punched-card methods to production control, Sciaky has derived many benefits, among them the following:

1. The volume of the firm's business has tripled without any increase in the number of employees in production control.

2. Stores inventory has been reduced by $1 million. In manufacturing to customers' specifications as Sciaky does, these inventories can always get out of control without an effective system. Under previous methods, the company had to stock as many as 15,000 components for a single piece of equipment. At one time, it discovered a three-year supply of unneeded nuts and bolts. On another occasion, it discovered a ten-year supply of resistors that were fast becoming obsolete. Now, with purchasing based on reports derived from the punched-card system, obsolescence has become a negligible factor.

3. The paperwork flow time required to process a manufacturing order has been reduced from one to two weeks to twelve to fourteen hours. As a result, delivery times have been shortened without disrupting schedules.

4. The use of testing facilities can now be properly planned. Consequently, final checkouts of the various products can be expedited, and machines do not accumulate on the plant floor before shipment.

1-7. MORTGAGE LOAN ACCOUNTING ON PUNCHED CARDS

Dime Savings Bank of Brooklyn, Brooklyn, New York, handles about seventy-five thousand mortgages, with approximately sixty-nine thousand of these on a monthly basis. In addition, it conducts a regular savings-bank business, consisting of deposits, Christmas Club, safe deposit boxes, etc.

Installation (IBM): Two card punches, four sorters, two collators, four accounting machines (two 403, one 405, one 419), calculating punch, three reproducing punches, five transfer-posting machines.

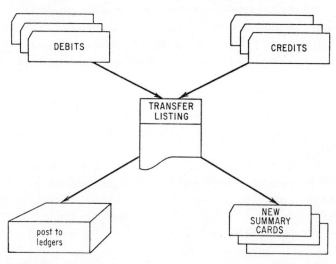

Exhibit 7-1. Mortgage loan accounting procedure, in general outline.

The bank's use of punched cards in mortgage loan accounting begins immediately after the closing papers have been completed with the mortgagor. One of the closing papers is the *mortgage information sheet.* This document takes different forms, depending on whether the mortgage is for a building loan, new loan, or conversion loan (normally, a change of status from builder to owner). The basic information for mortgage accounting is, however, the same in each case, and it is this document which provides information for the mortgage master cards.

To distribute the mortgage accounting work load throughout the month, monthly payment mortgages are set up on a three-cycle basis, with about thirty-four thousand falling due on the first of the month, twenty thousand on the eleventh, and fifteen thousand on the twenty-first. Billing notices for the various cycles are distinguished by different-colored punched cards and by punched codes.

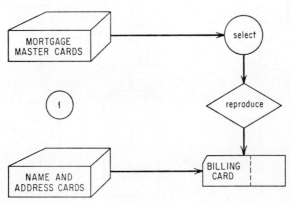

Exhibit 7-2

Mortgage Loan Procedure. The mortgage master card for each mortgage is keypunched with the cycle number, along with the mortgage number, type of loan, type of property, county, interest rate, and other pertinent data. To ensure correctness of the master card, a printed list is run off on an accounting machine and proofread. The master cards are then run through the calculating punch to calculate interest and amortization.

An appraisal master card is created for the appraisal department, plus a name-and-address card. These cards are filed by mortgage number.

Assuming that a mortgage has been in effect for a full month, the following procedure is carried out to issue a bill to the mortgagor and to receive and record payment (paragraph numbers correspond to those on the accompanying flow charts) :

1. About ten days prior to the billing cutoff date for each cycle, the mortgage master card is used to reproduce information on a billing card. This covers account number, month due, total amount due, and special codes. Through the use of a *comparing bill feed* on the

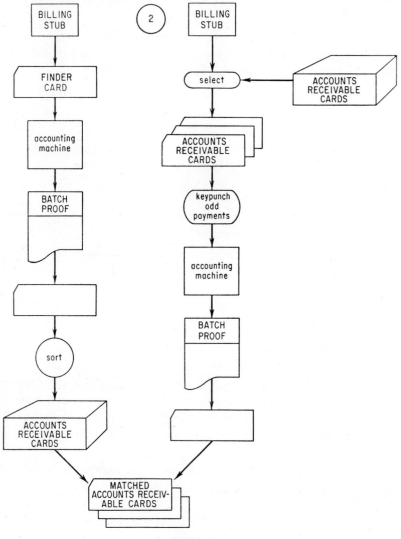

Exhibit 7-3

accounting machine, the billing card is printed with the mortgagor's
name and address from the name-and-address card. A trial balance
is taken from the master mortgage cards, after which accounts receivable cards are created.

In the event of any arrears, a punched card is reproduced and
merged with the accounts receivable card, along with any debit cards
indicating payments for taxes, insurance, etc. This accumulated finan-

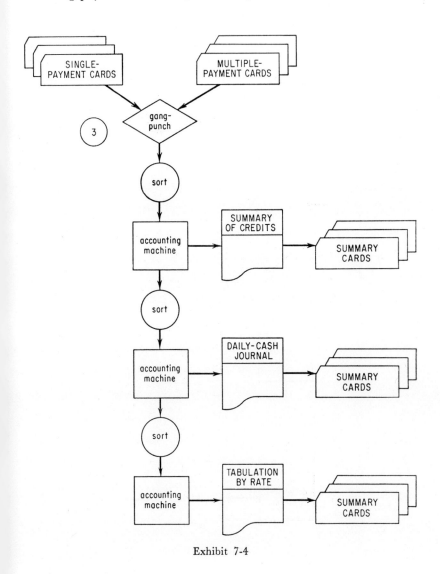

Exhibit 7-4

cial information is printed on the billing card by the accounting machine.

The billing card is a normal-sized punched card with a perforated punched stub. The stub is returned with the payment. The main portion, retained by the mortgagor, contains explanations of charges, principal balance, escrow balance, interest, amortization, dates, and amounts of various taxes paid by the bank, and codes indicating reasons for various charges.

2. When the stub and payment arrive in the bank, they go first to the accounting department, where check totals are balanced against totals shown on stubs. If everyone paid the exact amount listed on the statement, the accounting procedure would be quite simple. There are, however, persons who make advance payments on principal and taxes and those who make only partial payments, etc. On single-item payments—those paying the specified amount—it is necessary only to

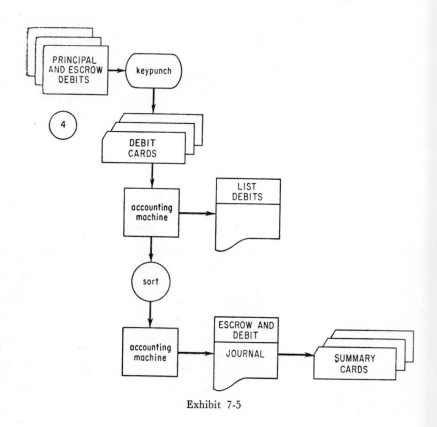

Exhibit 7-5

reproduce a finder card from the statement stub and match it to the accounts receivable card kept on file. In the case of multiple-item payments (right-hand side of flow chart), the accounts receivable card is selected manually from the file and punched with the odd payments.

3. A summary is then run for the mortgage servicing department showing arrears payments. Other summaries, run by due date and by rate, are prepared for audit control. Journal listings, by cycle, are also prepared.

4. During this time, any escrow (tax) or principal debits that are paid are keypunched and filed by mortgage number.

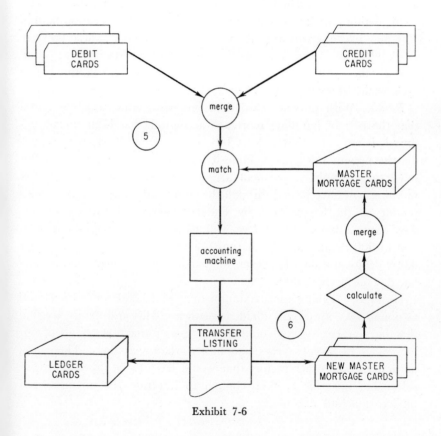

Exhibit 7-6

5. These debit cards are merged with the credit payment cards and matched against the master mortgage card for accuracy. The

debits appear on the following month's statement sent to the mortgagor.

Following this step, a transfer-posting list is prepared on an accounting machine. This list is used to post individual mortgage ledger cards and is the permanent file on each mortgage containing all information from the time the mortgage is taken out until it is paid.

6. As the transfer-posting list is being prepared, a new master mortgage card is created as a by-product. This new master contains constant data (listed above), plus new balances, date, and fixed billing amounts. The old and new master cards are run through the accounting machine to obtain a tabulation for proof purposes. The new cards are printed with punched data in an interpreter and then run through a calculating punch to calculate new interest and amortization figures. The new master cards are filed by mortgage number, where they are available for answering requests regarding mortgage status.

With the creation of the new mortgage master card, the billing cycle begins all over again.

Results. With punched-card data processing, the bank has found that the cost of handling mortgage accounting has been sharply reduced. It estimates that at least 100 persons would be needed to handle the present mortgage volume if manual methods were used. But now, for example, a payment arriving in the office on a Monday morning will have passed through the entire procedure, complete with posting on the ledger card, by Tuesday afternoon. "On an average day," says a bank official, "we will handle 3,500 credits and from 300 to 500 debits. These can run to a maximum of 8,500 credits or 8,000 debits in a day. However, the maximum combined total for any one day has been 13,000."

He adds, "Taking the maximum total of 13,000 transactions and assuming they are evenly divided between credits and debits, we find that our present system could handle one transaction on all of our mortgages of twenty years ago in less than two days. There are, naturally, some other factors that would have to be taken into consideration, but this is close enough to illustrate the advantage of modern machine accounting."

The Case Book — Part II

This section of the case book describes applications of *computers,* or electronic data processing machines. The applications involve four types of these units: the IBM Ramac 305 (two cases), Remington Rand's Univac File-Computer, and the IBM 1401. Although there are several other types of units being used for business data processing, these three were chosen chiefly to illustrate some of the capabilities of electronic systems.

All the companies mentioned in the following cases were veteran users of standard punched-card installations. They made the conversion to the electronic systems for one main reason: the need for greater data processing capacity brought on by the growth of the business. Although each might have, with the addition of some units and some procedural changes, been able to continue with its punched-card system for routine data processing, it found this system no match for the electronic machines in providing management information.

This is, in itself, significant. Punched-card data processing had taught the management of each of these firms the value of analyses of business data. As each firm grew and its management problems multiplied, the need for more decision-making information became evident. Thus, as one company official points out: "We wanted to use our computer as a management tool, to benefit from its ability to make logical choices given alternatives during the processing of information, rather than simply as a device for speeding existing paperwork procedures."

This attitude can be noted in company after company that makes the change from a standard punched-card installation to an electronic system. The principal desire is to harness the electronic system's speed and logical ability for management purposes. One is entitled to conjecture, however, whether the success of American Bosch in applying the total-system approach to manufacturing control does not derive as much from its previous experience with a punched-card system as from its use of an electronic unit. In other words, it was this first experience which posed the possibilities and the Ramac 305 which enabled them to be realized.

Some emphasis has been placed in this section on electronic units having large file-storage capacities with random access. Many other units becoming available to business are being designed with this characteristic, because the growing need in business is for systems able to store the files of the company: data relating to inventory, customers, vendors, parts, raw materials, financial records, etc. As a firm grows and more and more of these file data become involved in analyses for management use, it faces the problem of punched-card volume. For Big Bear Stores to keep a punched-card record of its inventory of 6,000 different items, for example, would require many thousands of cards; to gain access to the data in these cards would require considerable machine time. Although a computer can solve the problems of storage and access, the punched card is still important as input and output. Nevertheless, the trend toward random-access computers with large file storage will continue, thus filling a pressing requirement of business data processing.

2-1. IN-LINE PROCESSING WITH IBM RAMAC 305

In the rush toward fast, accurate punched-card data processing, one advantage of manual clerical methods has had to be left behind—what International Business Machines Corporation calls *in-line processing*, or the posting of each transaction as it occurs. For example, under manual methods, when an item is withdrawn from inventory for shipment to a customer, all the ledger accounts affected are changed accordingly. Moreover, the clerks have random access to each account; that is, they can reach and alter each account in any sequence. This method of data processing has had to be sacrificed with punched cards because, to make use of the mass production idea, the processing had to be done in batches. Thus, transactions of a like kind are allowed to accumulate before being processed on punched cards; they cannot be efficiently processed and posted singly.

IBM's Ramac 305 may be said to bring the office full circle, in that it revives in-line methods amid full mechanization. The Ramac permits each record to be updated at the time data pertaining to a transaction are being processed.

The name *Ramac* is a contraction of *random-access method of accounting and control.* The unit is essentially a self-contained data processing system containing most of the components of a standard punched-card installation. The heart of the Ramac 305 is a disk memory storing up to 10 million characters of alphabetical and numerical data on 50 steel disks rotating on a vertical spindle. On each disk are 10 sectors, 5 on the top surface and 5 on the bottom. Each sector contains, depending on the disk memory's capacity, 100 or 200 tracks, each track storing 100 alphanumerical characters in the form of magnetic spots. Access to these data is by means of an *access arm* with a forked read-write head, which can reach any desired track on the top or bottom of any disk in a matter of milliseconds. Thus, any data stored in the disk memory are almost instantly accessible—and at random.

Built around this disk memory are the other data processing components.

Processing Unit: This is the operating core of the Ramac 305, a drum with magnetic tracks for the machine's stored program, working storage, arithmetic, typewriter, output, and input. It may be called the "clearinghouse" of the system, providing a place where data can be stored and manipulated during processing.

Card Reader: This unit translates the punched card's coding into electric impulses, which are stored on the input tracks of the processing unit (above). From here the impulses are transferred to the magnetic-core unit, which actuates the access arm to retrieve data from or write data in the disk memory.

Output Printer: Data withdrawn from the disk memory by the access arm are transmitted back through the magnetic core to the output tracks of the processing unit. The output printer is actuated to write the data in the form of a record, such as an invoice.

Card Punch: This is the summary-punching unit of the Ramac. As transactions are processed and printed, the card punch produces simultaneously cards for each line of printed output or summarizing the record being printed.

Control Console: This component consists in a keyboard, an electric typewriter, signal lights, and control keys. The Ramac operator can, through the keyboard, inquire into the status of any record stored in the disk memory, and the required information will be automatically written out by the electric typewriter.

In the following two cases, the Ramac 305 is shown handling the kind of data processing job for which it was designed: retrieving and updating large quantities of information. In the first case, the use of a Ramac by a supermarket chain is described. In the second case, a manufacturer's use of the Ramac for manufacturing control is explained.

Supermarket Management with Ramac 305

Big Bear Stores Company, Columbus, Ohio, is a supermarket chain operating 27 stores within a 145-mile radius of Columbus. The company's annual sales volume exceeds $75 million.

Equipment: Ramac 305 data processing machine, two 407 accounting machines (operating off-line with the Ramac), two card punches, one verifier, two sorters, two collators, one interpreter, two card-order converters, two reproducing punches.

Several years ago, to correct the inadequacies of manual order processing and billing, Big Bear began using punched-card data processing. As a result, the company's 250,000-square-foot warehouse was reorganized so that items were located according to their rate of movement. A slot location system was introduced to speed handling; each item and pallet is marked with a four-digit slot number.

The punched-card system provided inventory control information that was previously unobtainable except through a periodic physical count. Purchasing records were changed from buyers' manually posted books to a mechanically posted ledger card system. Further, the system resulted in an improvement in the ordering of seasonal items and in a reduction of out-of-stock conditions.

But the full benefits of the new system were not felt at the individual store level. Store managers were still confronted with unbalanced inventories because of the considerable time lag between the ordering and receiving of merchandise. Consequently, store ordering methods were converted to a mark sense card system. The store manager uses a magnetic lead pencil to indicate on cards what items are required. The cards are sent to Columbus, where the pencil marks are automatically converted into punched holes in the cards. With the elimination of manual card punching, merchandise can be delivered from the warehouse to the store within forty-eight hours.

As the store chain grew, however, the need for expanded data processing facilities became apparent. After investigation, Big Bear became the first grocery chain to install the Ramac 305.

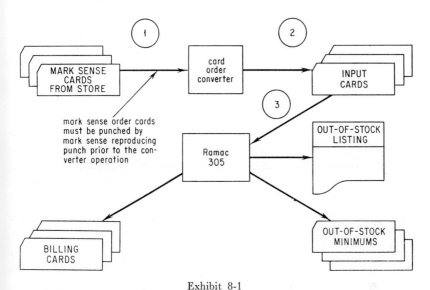

Exhibit 8-1

Order Processing and Invoicing. The disk-memory unit of the Ramac contains all the relevant data for each of the 10,000 items warehoused in Columbus. Order data introduced into the machine on cards punched from the mark sense cards result in the inventory levels of various items being altered and in other data being read out in the form of punched cards for the preparation of invoices. Below is a general description of the procedure (paragraph numbers correspond to those on the accompanying flow charts):

1. Using a merchandise catalogue, the store manager marks the desired order quantity for each item on a mark sense store order card.

2. When received in Columbus, the cards are converted to punched cards and thence to input cards.

3. These input cards contain sheet number of the merchandise catalogue, line numbers, and quantity for as many as 17 items. Other input cards representing new items, receipts into stock, adjustments, or miscellaneous charge cards are used to update the data contained in the disk memory.

As it senses each input order card, the Ramac searches the item record in the disk memory for stock availability, updates the inventory balance and shipments to date, accumulates cost and retail value of shipments, and produces a fully extended billing card.

During this routine, the machine also controls the selection of specific price data from the four retail price zones, initiates a partial shipment when there is insufficient stock on hand, or authorizes the substitution of manufacturers' deals for regular merchandise.

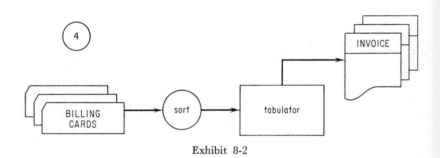

Exhibit 8-2

4. The billing cards contain all the data required to print an invoice. After being sorted to warehouse location, the cards are run through the accounting machine to obtain a three-part invoice for use as a warehouse selection sheet, a store invoice, and an accounting department record.

While the billing cards are being produced, the Ramac printer writes an out-of-stock listing for each store, showing merchandise ordered but unavailable for shipment. Additional cards are punched during the billing routine for items that have reached a minimum or out-of-stock level; these signal cards are interpreted and forwarded to buyers for action.

5. Once a week, stock-status cards are punched from the data collected in the Ramac 305's memory. These cards are run through an accounting machine that prints a stock-status report and are used to update the buyers' ledger cards mechanically.

The data in the disk memory are also used to prepare management activity reports, gross profit summaries, and various other reports for management's use.

Results. The installation of the Ramac has enabled Big Bear to maintain a consistent rate of expansion and improve inventory turn-

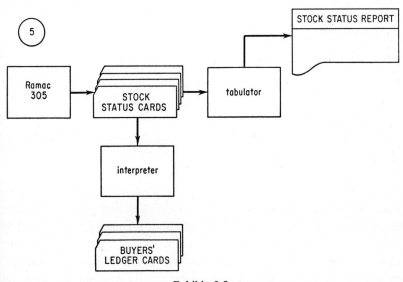

Exhibit 8-3

over to a considerable extent. Also, the company has been able to add six stores to its chain without adding to its data processing facilities. Yet the speed of paperwork has been increased. Order processing from all the company's stores is started at 7:30 A.M., and by 9:30 the warehouse has started to fill orders. Soon after, the whole order-writing and billing job is completed, leaving the remainder of the day free for the preparation of reports needed for improved management planning and control.

Manufacturing Control with the Ramac 305

American Bosch Division, American Bosch Arma Corporation, Springfield, Massachusetts, is the leading United States manufacturer of diesel fuel injection equipment, marketing over 1,000 end products and 6,000 service parts through direct contact with customers. Employing 1,800 persons in the Springfield area, the division maintains four regional warehouses and 50 distributors throughout the United States.

Installation (IBM): Ramac 305 data processing machine, with 407 accounting machine operating on-line in place of 370 printer.

For over seventeen years, American Bosch had used a punched-card system for manufacturing control. With it, a new production schedule for 10,000 end products and manufactured parts, represented by 40,000 bill-of-material cards, had been produced monthly. This schedule reflected all changes in orders, forecasts, and bills of material in the preceding thirty days. Satisfactory as this system was, management felt that certain refinements should be made to the data processing procedures to keep pace with increasing customer demand and the factory modernization program.

One planned refinement was to reflect changes as they occurred, thus eliminating critical situations requiring "crash" conferences of key personnel. Also, if more current inventory records were available, items needed to build an end product or subassembly but currently unavailable could be scheduled for production just prior to the date required. Under the punched-card method, for example, shop orders had been issued up to forty days in advance of the starting date so that the shop could determine what was not available in inventory. When orders were changed before the production starting date, all the paperwork affecting these orders had to be traced back and changed. Management felt, finally, that, if additional usage and historical data could be accumulated, it would be possible to produce items in more economical quantities, thus reducing ordering and shop setup costs.

The System Is Studied. The American Bosch management made a study of all factors affecting the manufacturing control application. First, they determined that their system should be able to process effectively, with little outside intervention, varying types of input, including all material transactions, engineering changes, service requirements, and production schedules by time period. Second, these input documents must be processed against internally stored records to do the following:

1. Convert product schedule to requirements by time period.

2. Measure requirements against on-hand, on-order, and reorder points for each inventory item to determine the time period when shop orders and purchase orders must be prepared.

3. Revise economical order quantities and reorder points by constant evaluation of the factors involved in their calculation.

4. Cancel and/or reschedule unreleased manufacturing or purchase orders.

Finally, the system must rapidly select from storage the data required to prepare the following items:

1. Status reports for all released manufacturing orders.

2. Shop orders to manufacture in economical size lots by time period, indicating standard costs for all components.

3. Stock planning status for any part on request.

4. Evaluation of optimum inventory based on economical order quantities and reorder points.

5. Immediate answers to questions concerning any part in inventory.

Why the Ramac Was Chosen. Many features of the Ramac 305 recommended it for the application requirements summarized above. For example, the Ramac's storage capacity—10 million characters— was more than adequate to maintain the inventory records for the 15,000 finished goods, assemblies, and parts, a bill of material for every manufactured item, and the quantities of each part needed to satisfy orders and forecasts by time period.

Again, the random-access ability of the machine would allow the updating of inventory records on a current basis and would also provide the most direct method of exploding the production schedule down to its individual requirements. Moreover, this would be accomplished in a single pass through the system. Finally, the inquiry feature of the machine would make up-to-date facts available on any part as it progressed through production.

The New Procedure in Outline. In adopting its new manufacturing control procedure, American Bosch has striven toward a *management operating system,* whereby six basic functions of a manufacturing company are integrated with one another. This is an application of the total-system approach, which recognizes that the flow of relevant data through a company must be uninterrupted and, so far as possible, automatic. In a word, American Bosch's procedure puts into practice the idea that the output data of one function becomes the input data to the next.

Here is the sequence of data flow from function to function:

1. A *forecast* enters the system as input, where sales history is ap-

plied by formula. The output is the finished product plan. (Management provides a forecast of end items extending over a given time period. Since an end item or product is made up of a combination of devices or special features, the end-item forecast is adjusted by sales history to determine the mix of the devices needed. The output, consequently, is the finished product plan.)

2. *Materials planning* begins as the finished product plan is passed against the bills of material, producing as output the requirements for raw materials, parts, and assemblies. (The bills of material, which are stored in the Ramac, are descriptive listings of parts and materials needed to manufacture various products. The bills of material are analyzed and computed from the top level of finished products down to the lowest level of items needed.)

At this point, the total material requirements *without* regard to inventory have been determined.

3. *Inventory management* is conducted concurrently with materials planning. Material requirements are checked against inventory, which is stored in the Ramac disk memory, and planned orders are initiated for quantities according to established ordering factors.

(The material requirements must be adjusted so that plant orders represent optimum production quantities. Materials in inventory carry ordering factors such as minimum-maximum values or economic ordering quantities, which provide the proper adjustments. Ordering factors take into account the usage, the cost, and the best production techniques for each item.)

With the creation of planned orders, the over-all planning of materials, which began with the sales forecast, is now complete.

4. *Scheduling* takes each order and plans it according to master operations and loading formulas. Master operations are predetermined units of work stored in the Ramac memory and are the units required to produce a part. The operation hours are planned by work center and by time period, according to the loading formulas. This forms the manufacturing plan.

(The manufacturing plan is progressively broken down and given to production personnel for action as shop orders with accompanying labor tickets, move tickets, raw material requisitions, etc.)

5. *Dispatching* puts the manufacturing plan into action according to *shop status*. Shop status is the progress made on active orders, operation by operation, as reported from the shop and stored in the sys-

tem. Each work center has normally more than one plant order ready to be worked on, and the priority of plant orders is constantly changing due to (1) delivery dates, (2) shop order cost representing company's investment in item, (3) the need to replenish inventory, or (4) the lateness or earliness of the shop order with respect to its schedule.

Each plant order is checked against all other orders in relation to shop status, and optimum work priorities for orders at all work centers are automatically determined. Thus, the plant's manufacturing plan is adjusted daily. This results in reducing the amount of work in process, better use of machines, and on-time deliveries to customers.

6. *Operations evaluation,* the final function, monitors the preceding five functions. Any variations in forecasting, materials planning, inventory management, scheduling, or dispatching are determined automatically and promptly reported to management on an exception basis. Operating data from these five functions are passed against controls (budgets, standard costs, standard operation times, work center capacities) stored in the Ramac. The resulting evaluation information enables management to learn how efficiently material, machines, manpower, and money are being employed.

American Bosch's Procedure. Although it envisions having the above six functions processed by the Ramac, American Bosch is processing only sales forecasts, materials management, and inventory management on the system.

The procedures described below are based on a method of level-by-level net-requirements planning. This means that in the plant and within the Ramac the various parts that go into the products manufactured by the firm are divided into successive levels. At the lowest level are raw materials. Above these are the component parts fabricated from the raw materials and purchased parts. At the next level are minor assemblies, subassemblies built from the components, and major assemblies made from the subassemblies. At the top level are the finished products made up of the various major assemblies. Since any given product may make use of an assembly used in many other end products and may also use raw materials used in other products, it follows that an order for one type of product could affect the supply of materials needed for other products. What the Ramac does, simply, is to check down through the level-by-level structure of the firm's bills of material (stored in the disk memory) to see what must be done at each level to satisfy the order. If it finds, for example, a shortage of raw material, the machine issues a warning whereupon management will expedite purchase of the material.

Material Transactions. There are 24 different types of material transactions processed through the Ramac. These can be generally classified as receipts, adjustments, and issues. The Ramac recognizes the type of transaction by code in the card being read and selects the correct records. For each of the 15,000 items (1,000 end products, 9,000 manufactured parts, 5,000 purchased parts), there are five 100-character records in the disk memory. The first two records are used for storing inventory and cost data.

As each type of material card is read, the inventory record for that item is selected and the on-hand balance, usage to date, or last activity date is updated. Below is the programmer's chart of the inventory and cost records stored in the Ramac's memory.

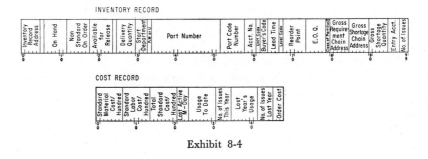

Exhibit 8-4

Located next to these two records is a requirements record, indicating the number of pieces actually required for each of 20 ten-day periods.

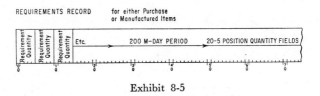

Exhibit 8-5

The fourth record stores commitments by time period. These reflect the quantity to be ordered to cover requirements. Since these commitments are for the manufacture of economical lot quantities, they will differ from requirement amounts.

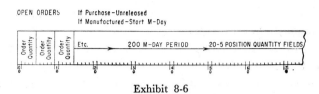

Exhibit 8-6

The last record of 100 characters in the disk memory is either a bill of material (if the product is manufactured) or released orders to a vendor (if the item is purchased).

Level-by-level Net-requirements Planning. Above were described the constant data stored in the Ramac's disk memory. Against these data are passed variable data in the form of customers' orders and the sales forecast. As noted previously, the Ramac will signal the status of each item in face of the orders and forecast. In the following descrip-

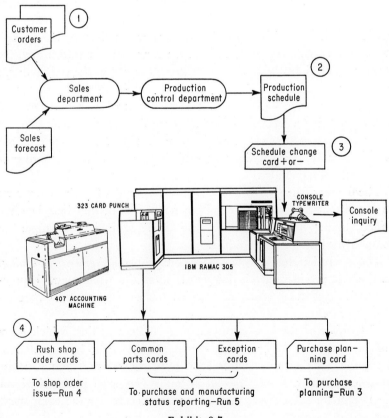

Exhibit 8-7

tion of the procedure, the paragraph numbers correspond to those on the accompanying flow charts:

1. Customers' orders are received and sales forecasts are prepared by the sales department.

2. The sales department and the production control department working together determine the production schedule changes (increases or decreases) by time period, indicating what end products are now currently required to satisfy the forecast and customer orders. In addition, they also indicate those items which are required to satisfy the aftermarket business.

3. This schedule is then introduced into the Ramac in the form of schedule-change cards (plus or minus). It is important to note that this is a changed schedule of end products and not of parts and assemblies required to build those products.

As each change card is read, the Ramac internally finds the inventory record for the required end product. The on-hand and on-order portion of the record is checked to determine whether there is enough stock to satisfy the requirement. If there is not sufficient inventory, the Ramac determines the lead time, stores the order in the requirements record for release at the proper time, and examines the bill-of-material record for the item to determine the quantities of each part required to build the item. This 100-character record will accommodate up to eight different component parts. If more than eight items are required in an assembly, the machine stores this information in an unused portion of the disk memory.

The Ramac then posts the quantity required of each component part or subassembly to the requirements record of that item by time period, taking into account the lead time required to assemble the components into the end product.

The operation to this point is called *gross-requirements planning.* As the last production schedule card enters the Ramac and is processed, the system automatically begins the *level-by-level net-requirements planning.*

This involves the consideration of each item against which gross requirements or changes in gross requirements have been posted to determine whether these items have sufficient inventory on hand or on order. If there is not sufficient inventory, an order is placed within the system for later release. The inventory record for the component part or subassembly is examined to determine whether there is sufficient inventory of its component parts or whether an order is required. This process continues for each part.

4. As a by-product of this routine, varying types of cards are created by the Ramac's card punch. The first of these, rush shop order cards, are punched if a given part should have been started before the current Manufacturing Day.[1] Whenever there is a requirement to order common parts, a common-part order card is punched. Because common parts are relatively inexpensive and used in large numbers, they are planned by the production control department and not by the Ramac. A purchase planning card is punched at the completion of the level-by-level routine to initiate the planning of the purchased items.

Also, exception cards for certain types of activity not planned by the Ramac are created:

a. Special engineering parts

b. Parts with economical order quantity (EOQ) but no reorder point (indicating usage last year but not this year)

c. Parts with reorder point but no EOQ (usage this year but none last year)

d. Parts with no reorder point and no EOQ (no usage this year or last year)

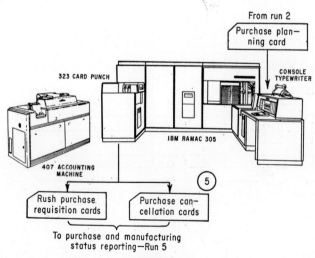

Exhibit 8-8

[1] Manufacturing Day refers to a calendar used by American Bosch, which assigns a numerical value to each working day of a month, the value indicating what the Ramac shows are the manufacturing requirements for that particular day.

5. The single purchase planning card is introduced into the Ramac. This card indicates one end of a chain that the Ramac has established within its disk memory, linking together all purchased items that have had any activity due to the explosion of the production schedule.

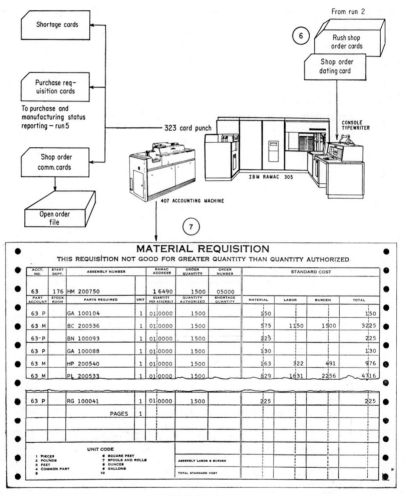

Exhibit 8-9

The Ramac proceeds to each item in this chain to determine if sufficient inventory is on hand or on order to satisfy the requirement. If inventory is not on hand, a purchase requisition is stored in the Ramac after consideration of the time required to obtain this item (lead time). If the date of the purchase requisition is prior to the current Manufacturing Day, a rush requisition card is created.

The Ramac proceeds in this fashion from this item to the next through the whole chain. As a result of a reduction or a revision in the production schedule due to changing customer requirements, previously established purchase requisitions may be canceled. In this case, a purchase cancellation card is punched.

The Ramac now contains the completed new manufacturing and purchase schedule in disk storage by M Day.

6. The system is now prepared to issue production orders to the shop for the current period. To do this, two types of cards are introduced: (1) rush shop order cards and (2) single shop order dating card indicating to the system the time period within which orders are now being issued.

The Ramac then searches the open-order portion of each record in the disk memory for the time period indicated. When it finds a quantity, it performs the two functions indicated in the next step.

7. If the part is manufactured, a complete material requisition or shop order is printed out, indicating the part and quantity to be made, its components, parts, and quantities, standard costs, and the start and finish M Days. A commitment card is punched for each shop order and is placed in an off-line open-order file. On completion of manufacturing, this card is reintroduced into the Ramac to reduce the open-order quantity. Shortage cards are punched for any component parts not in stock at the present time.

The second function involves this procedure if a part is purchased. Purchase requisition cards are punched, and these become the authority for a purchase order. The released order record is updated.

8. Using the indicated source information as input to the Ramac, a status report is printed every ten days for each active purchased and manufactured part. This report indicates the heading information, requirements, unreleased orders by M Day, and released orders by M Day (purchased parts only).

Results. According to American Bosch management, the above procedures have resulted in tangible savings for the company.

• With automatic control of economic order quantity procedures, the number of shop orders processed each year has already been cut by 4,000. It costs the firm $30 to prepare an order.

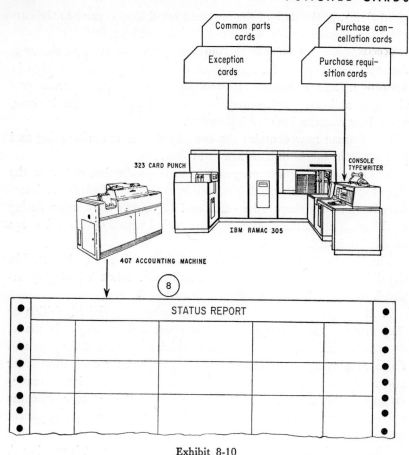

Exhibit 8-10

• As a by-product of this reduction, machine setup costs—ranging from $20 to $100 each—have been reduced.

• Standardized production levels will result in better planning of manpower requirements. Inventory, rather than employment, will fluctuate; and inventory dollars are being concentrated on active sales items.

• Production schedule changes can now be entered into the system immediately.

• Annually, the system will be able to handle automatically the task of working out cost revisions, thereby reducing the cost of this operation by 70 per cent.

2-2. PRODUCTION SCHEDULING WITH UNIVAC FILE-COMPUTER

William Carter Company, Needham Heights, Massachusetts, is the largest United States manufacturer of knitted underwear, with six mills in Georgia, Massachusetts, and Mississippi turning out 40 million garments in 600 styles annually. The firm receives between 800 and 1,000 new orders daily.

Installation (Remington Rand): Univac File-Computer (Model I) system consisting in card read-punch unit, five magnetic-tape units, high-speed printer, central computer, storage and electronic control units.

For many years, the company used a punched-card installation for much of its data processing, but the increased volume of business that developed during the 1950s made a larger system necessary. From the start, the company was determined to exploit the potential of electronic data processing to the fullest. It wanted to use the computer as a management tool: to benefit from its ability to make logical choices given alternatives during the processing of information rather than to use it simply as a device for speeding existing paperwork procedures.

The File-Computer System. The main feature of the system is the magnetic-drum storage for filing constant data. These data can be retrieved, altered, and put in storage in random sequence. As many as 10 drums, each holding up to 180,000 characters of data, can be used. In Carter's case, 6 drums contain the item inventory file and pertinent customer information:

A. *Item inventory file for each of 7,000 items*
   Inventory   Price
   Order demand by shipping month   Weight per garment
   Back orders available by priority Remaining to be sold (if
                                          discontinued item)
B. *By customer*—special shipping and invoicing requirements

Functioning around this central file are the other components of the system. The card read-punch unit introduces data into the system and also punches cards containing output data. The central computer, or arithmetic unit, performs addition, subtraction, multiplication, and division. Output in the form of printed records and reports is prepared by the printer, operating at the rate of 600 lines per minute. The magnetic-tape units are used to provide an alternative means of data input

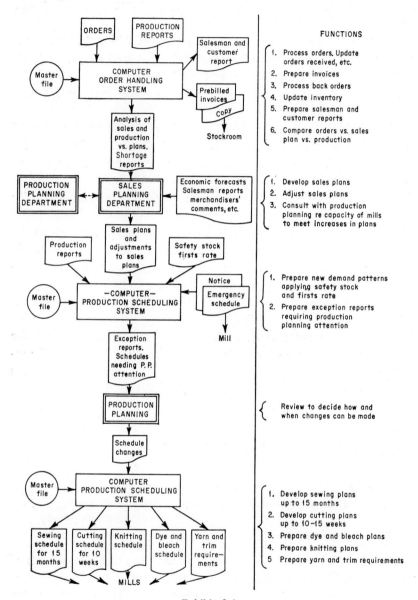

Exhibit 9-1

and output; for example, in Carter's order processing procedure, back-order information is recorded on magnetic tape for later summarizing.

Order Processing. Carter's order processing system features (*a*) prebilling of all customer orders "at once," "advance," and "back orders"; (*b*) completely automatic stock allocation to all orders (finished goods inventory is wholly controlled by the computer); (*c*) automatic magnetic-tape processing of all back orders and advance orders; and (*d*) complete order analysis for subsequent reports. It begins with the receipt of orders from the company's salesmen and from customers. After these orders are edited and rewritten, they are passed to card-punch operators, who pull prepunched customer name cards and style-color cards from tub files. The cards are punched with quantities ordered and then verified. These cards then become the input to the File-Computer. In one pass, the machine automatically:

1. Prepares a detailed, fully extended invoice with indication of discontinued and back-ordered items.

2. Prepares shipping labels.

3. Records all sales figures for subsequent analysis.

4. Records all back orders on magnetic tape and summarizes them on the magnetic drums.

5. Prepares a magnetic tape of invoiced items for subsequent analysis.

In this single run, several of the computer's capabilities are used—not only its ability to digest and process data in random sequence, but also its ability to make logical decisions between given alternatives and to carry out appropriate instructions for whichever condition is indicated. For example, some 30 to 40 per cent of the company's incoming orders are for future shipment, often months in advance. When processing such an order, the computer will refer it to future rather than current inventory, earmarking the right quantities of the right items to assure and protect their availability when the required date comes up.

Another refinement of the program assures that no more than three separate shipments will be made to fill any order. If the order cannot be filled completely from current warehouse stocks (data which are stored in the file), the computer arranges for part of it to be filled and shipped, but it makes sure that complete size ranges are shipped in the first shipment. Moreover, it guarantees automatically that not less than 25 per cent of the total is shipped initially against an advance

order. It then arranges for a second shipment at the earliest possible
date, consisting of not less than 50 per cent of the remaining order,
and, if necessary, for a third and final shipment after that. It will also
automatically cancel small portions of the order when they have been
too long in the back-order file.

Many of the firm's customers have special invoice requirements
(some request that parcels carry no insurance, some wish a duplicate
copy of the invoice enclosed as packing slip, etc.), which the computer
automatically takes care of. It also calculates the weight and postal
charges of parcel post to each shipment.

The main result of the new system is the earlier availability and
greater comprehensiveness of management reports. Sales analysis figures, for example, are broken down according to the month of requested shipment. A weekly report is prepared showing the trend of
current order receipts compared to plans. This progress report gives
the sales forecasting and production scheduling departments a clear
picture of current and future demands and enables them to adjust
schedules to meet these demands. Monthly shipment reports are available up to two weeks earlier than was possible under the previous
system. Also, more detailed reports offer the sales department a better
opportunity of analyzing the effectiveness of the sales effort. Further, by studying accurate reports of total back orders (taken from the
memory drums), the firm has now an up-to-date picture of current
demands.

Carter's is just beginning to appreciate the value of the computer's
speed and decision-making ability. Effort is now being directed toward having the computer take over a large part of the routine sales
projection function. Through its ability to detect and project sales
trends, the computer will help bring about considerable inventory
savings.

2-3. PAYROLL WITH THE IBM 1401

Wyman-Gordon Company, Worcester, Massachusetts, is one of the
world's largest manufacturers of closed die forgings. The firm special-
izes in large-sized components for the aircraft, missile, and automotive
industries, many of these components being forged in "exotic" alloys.
Some 4,000 workers are employed in plants in Worcester and North
Grafton, Massachusetts, and in Harvey, Illinois.

Installation (IBM): A card-reading 1401 data processing system (the first delivered to any manufacturing firm) is the key hardware. It consists in a 1401 processing unit, 1402 card read-punch unit, and 1403 printer.

Other punched-card equipment includes five card punches, five card verifiers, three sorters, interpreters, reproducing punch, two collators, 604 calculating punch, summary punch, two 407 accounting machines.

The 1401 data processing system is a new family of machines consisting of three basic configurations: (1) the card system, (2) the magnetic-tape system, and (3) the Ramac system. As noted above, Wyman-Gordon uses the card system and, at this writing, has the Ramac 1401 system on order.

The 1401 system's processing unit controls the entire system by means of its stored program and performs the arithmetic and logical operations. It contains also a console for external supervision of the system. Data are stored and manipulated by a magnetic-core unit.

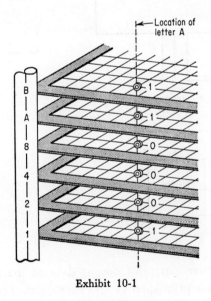

Exhibit 10-1

This unit consists of a series of tiny rings made of a magnetic material, through each of which run several electric wires. Current passing through the wires magnetizes each ring in a certain direction. Thus,

a core magnetized in one direction will contain a "bit" of data having
a value of 1, but when its magnetism is reversed, the value will be 0.
Consequently, when the rings are arranged in planes stacked one
above the other, the varying directions (or *polarities*) of their magnetic charges can designate the data making up numerical or alphabetical characters (see illustration, page 217).

The card read-punch unit is equipped with a read feed for the input of data from punched cards and also a punch feed for the output
of data in card form. The unit can read and punch cards simultaneously.

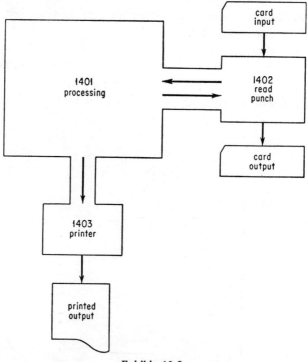

Exhibit 10-2

The 1403 printer can print output data at the rate of 600 lines
per minute, with a print span of 100 characters. The printing is performed by a chain device on which are fixed the various characters.
As this chain travels in a horizontal plane, each character to be printed
is positioned opposite a hammer that presses the form against the

chain. Before a character is printed, it is checked against the corresponding position in the print area of the magnetic core storage to ensure accuracy.

The 1401 system operates in response to a stored program, which is loaded into the machine by punched cards. Thus, the system is able to perform a procedure from beginning to end without manual intervention. The flow of data through the system is illustrated by the schematic drawing on page 218.

General Procedure. Wyman-Gordon's data processing department serves the two Massachusetts plants, processing about 150 various jobs and reports, many of them quite small. For maximum efficiency, every step of every job is documented, measured in fifteen-minute increments, and scheduled to a specific person and equipment, and performance is carefully measured and costed.

The 1401 was installed primarily to handle accounting, production control, and inventory. Because the company's financial operations were already on punched cards, some 20 of them were the first to be converted to the computer. These include payroll, accounts receivable, tool accounting (a complex task for space-age forgings), forging cost ledger, job costing (estimate versus actual), sales costing, machine utilization reports, property accounting, materials inventory, and electrical stores inventory.

The 1401 serves to reduce the card handling, machine steps, and time needed for processing each of these operations, and it provides more comprehensive reporting. Payroll, for example, required 47 machine operations on standard punched-card equipment and 12½ hours to process. Just five operations are required now, taking only 1½ hours. Of this, 1 hour is taken in card assembling.

Payroll Procedure. Job tickets from the North Grafton and Worcester forge plants (which have incentive plans) are sent to the data processing department daily. There, cards are keypunched with data on operator number, equipment number, number of setups, set and tryout hours, production hours, quantity produced, etc. These cards are fed into the 1401, which reads them and computes a detailed earnings record for each employee. The computer also punches payroll summary cards, one for each worker. Meanwhile, hourly information from attendance cards for nonincentive workers at both plants is also punched into cards.

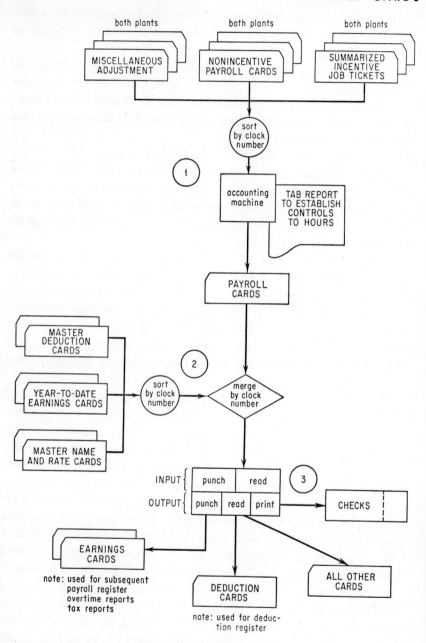

both plants   both plants   both plants

MISCELLANEOUS
ADJUSTMENT

NONINCENTIVE
PAYROLL CARDS

SUMMARIZED
INCENTIVE
JOB TICKETS

sort
by clock
number

①

accounting
machine

TAB REPORT
TO ESTABLISH
CONTROLS
TO HOURS

PAYROLL
CARDS

MASTER
DEDUCTION
CARDS

YEAR-TO-DATE
EARNINGS CARDS

MASTER NAME
AND RATE CARDS

②

sort
by clock
number

merge
by clock
number

INPUT { punch | read }   ③

OUTPUT { punch | read | print }   CHECKS

EARNINGS
CARDS

note: used for subsequent
payroll register
overtime reports
tax reports

DEDUCTION
CARDS

note: used for deduc-
tion register

ALL OTHER
CARDS

Exhibit 10-3

Thenceforth, the procedure is as follows (paragraph numbers correspond to those on accompanying flow chart):

1. The cards are sorted by clock or employee number and run through the accounting machine to obtain a listing for control purposes.

2. The incentive and nonincentive cards are sorted by employee number and collated with employee name cards, day-rate cards, master deduction cards, and previous year-to-date earnings cards and fed into the 1401.

3. The 1401 computes each worker's gross pay, consisting of regular earnings, special premium earnings, night premium earnings, overtime earnings, and holiday or allowed wages. From this it deducts federal and state income taxes, Social Security contributions, pension contributions, charitable contributions, etc., to arrive at net pay.

The 1401's output consists of a printed check and attached weekly earnings record for each employee (the earnings record is a punched card for reconciliation purposes) and an updated year-to-date earnings card for each employee. From the latter, a series of payroll reports are run on the 1401, including a deduction register, payroll register, overtime reports, etc.

Production Control. Still in the formative stage at this time is a production control procedure that the company hopes will solve some expensive problems common to many space-age vendors having large investments in specialized machinery, highly skilled labor, and expensive materials.

In general terms, Wyman-Gordon will first establish controls over its raw material inventory. Next, a standard practice sheet will be created, optimum scheduling and loading will be sought, priorities will be established, and improved dispatching procedures set up.

The initial system will involve generation of a work-in-progress card and a move ticket, which will relieve the work-in-progress card upon completion of the operation. Fed into the 1401, these will enable the company to produce daily reports on work in progress, operations completed, productivity, and daily shop schedules.

With the addition of the second 1401 with a Ramac disk memory, these same reports will be produced as a result of internally stored and updated information.

Results. In the area of financial accounting, Wyman-Gordon's computer has reduced processing time to about one-eighth of that formerly required, yet does a much more complete job, according to John L. McCarthy, data processing manager. This means that management now has detailed reports in hand in record time. For example, in the past, the punched-card equipment produced a series of cost reports that were manually posted to the forging cost ledger. This took about two hundred hours per month. Now the 1401 prints out the whole ledger in less than one hour.

Also, the reduction in card handling and machine steps has resulted in a corresponding reduction in errors. It could also result in a reduction of clerical personnel—if the firm chose to remain static in data processing. However, in view of Wyman-Gordon's expanding data processing horizons, this will not be the case.

Finally, the compact, transistorized computer has solved a space problem for the firm by increasing the volume of work performed in a minimum of floor space (250 square feet).

Bibliography

Books

Bell, William D.: *A Management Guide to Electronic Computers*, McGraw-Hill Book Company, Inc., New York, 1957.

Keller, I. Wayne: *Management Accounting for Profit Control*, McGraw-Hill Book Company, Inc., New York, 1957.

Kozmetsky, George, and Paul Kircher: *Electronic Computers and Management Control*, McGraw-Hill Book Company, Inc., New York, 1956.

Neuschel, Richard F.: *Management by System*, 2d ed., McGraw-Hill Book Company, Inc., New York, 1960.

Postley, John A.: *Computers and People*, McGraw-Hill Book Company, Inc., New York, 1960.

Publications

American Management Association: *Management's Broadening Responsibilities: A Profile of the Management Job*, General Management Series, no. 163, New York, 1953.

American Management Association: *Operations Research Reconsidered: Some Frontiers and Boundaries of Industrial OR*, Management Report no. 10, New York, 1958.

Division of Research, Graduate School of Business Administration, Harvard University: *Automatic Data Processing Conference*, Boston, 1956.

National Machine Accountants Association: *Data Processing—1959 Proceedings*, St. Louis, 1959.

Periodicals

"A Guide to Production Control," *American Machinist/Metalworking Manufacturing*, Sept. 19, 1960.

"Top Management Takes a Second Look at Electronic Data Processing," *Business Horizons,* Spring, 1959.

"Industrial Automatic Systems: Progress and Payout," *Control Engineering,* September, 1960.

"The Manager and the Black Box," *Harvard Business Review,* November–December, 1960.

"When the Computer Takes Over the Office," *Harvard Business Review,* July–August, 1960.

"No More Clerks in Purchasing," *Purchasing,* Oct. 24, 1960.

Glossary

Below are brief definitions of some terms used in data processing. These definitions are derived from those prepared by International Business Machines Corporation, the *Glossary of Automation Terms* published by the National Office Management Association, and the glossary appearing in *Programming Business Computers* by Daniel D. McCracken, Harold Weiss, and Tsai-Hwa Lee (John Wiley & Sons, Inc., New York, 1959).

Accounting Controls — Checks set up within and alongside an automatic data processing system as safeguards against error and fraud.

Analog Computer — A computer that solves problems by translating physical conditions like flow, temperature, or pressure into electrical quantities and using electric equivalent circuits for the physical phenomena. Used chiefly in scientific work. Cf. *Digital Computer* (q.v.).

Arithmetic Unit — The part of an electronic data processing machine which performs arithmetic operations and also permits the computer to take alternative course of action under predetermined conditions ("logical" operations).

Binary Number System — A system of numbers using a base of 2, so that quantities can be represented by zero (0) and one (1). The conventional decimal number system, in contrast, uses a base of 10. Since a computer represents data by the presence or absence of electronic signals, the binary notation has become the code or language of the computer, with 0 indicating the absence of a signal and 1 indicating the presence.

Card Column — One of the vertical divisions in a punched card, normally accommodating one letter, digit, or special character. The IBM card contains 80 columns. The Remington Rand card contains 45 columns divided horizontally into two "fields," making 90 columns.

Card Field — A column or columns reserved for the punching of data of a specific nature.

Check Digit — A digit in a "self-checking" code which is calculated from the remaining digits. Thus, if a digit in the code is incorrectly punched by card-punch operator, the error can be detected.

Coding — Assigning of letters, digits, or both to identify or classify data.

Collating — Interfiling or merging two sets of cards into one set of a given sequence. Both files of cards must be in the same sequence.

Comparing — Examination of fields (usually in two cards) for equality of data punched.

Constant Data — "Reference" or "file" information which is repeatedly used during the course of a firm's various transactions; e.g., names and addresses of customers and suppliers, names of employees, descriptions of items sold.

Control Panel — A removable panel containing an ordered array of terminals which may be interconnected by short electrical leads to instruct a machine to process data in a desired fashion. Also called a "plugboard" or "wiring panel."

Control Unit, or Console — The part of a computer giving an operator supervision over its operations.

Data Processing — The clerical routine entailed in the preparation of the firms operating records, accounting records, and management reports.

Detail Printing — The printing of one line of data from each card passing through the tabulator or accounting machine. Also called "listing."

Digital Computer — A data processing machine using numbers to express the variables and quantities of a problem. The numbers are usually expressed as a space–time distribution of punched holes in a card, electrical impulses, etc.

Duplicating — The automatic punching of data from one card into the next—normally performed on a card punch.

Electronic Data Processing Machine — A device that employs electronic circuitry to store and manipulate data; a computer.

Flow Chart — A graphical representation of a sequence of operations or procedures, using symbols to represent the various steps.

Gang Punching — Automatic copying of punched data from a master card into one or more cards that follow it. Where data change from one set of cards to the next, "interspersed" gang-punching methods may be used.

Group Printing — Machine summarizing of a group or groups of cards with one line printed for each group's totals and identifying data.

Input Unit — A device able to read recorded data (such as a punched card) and introduce them into a computer.

Integrated Data Processing — The method of recording original data at their point of origin in mechanical form, as in the preparation of a punched card containing data being simultaneously typed by a typewriter. This term is used in connection with common-language machines and is not synonymous with automatic data processing.

Interpreting — Printing on a punched card any or all of the data punched in it.

Magnetic Core — A tiny ring of ferromagnetic material which can be magnetized by wire running through it. Reversing the direction of the current changes the magnetic state of the core. Thus the two states can be used to represent 0 or 1, plus or minus, yes or no, on or off conditions. For machine purposes, this is the basis of the binary system (q.v.) of storing information.

Memory Unit — That part of a computer which, depending on its design, stores the program, intermediate results (if computation and processing), various constant data, etc. Also called "storage unit."

Output Unit — A device that produces the results of a computer's processing in the form of punched cards, printed records, etc.

Program — A complete plan of attack on a specific problem, including flow charts and a computer routine.

Random Access — The ability of an electronic data processing machine quickly to retrieve data in any sequence from storage.

Reproducing — The automatic punching of data from one set of cards into another set.

Sorting — Grouping cards in numerical or alphabetical sequence according to any classification punched in them.

Source Document — The original paper on which are recorded the details of a transaction.

Summary Punching — The automatic process of punching one card containing data summarized from a group of cards.

Tabulating — Cf. *Group Printing.*

Transaction — Any dealing involving the discharge of an obligation which a company may have with its customers, vendors, employees, stockholders, and government.

Variable Data — Information which is created by a transaction and which is unique to that transaction alone; e.g., quantity of items ordered by a customer. Cf. *Constant Data.*

Verifying — Checking the accuracy of data punched in a card with the data appearing in the source document.

Index

229

DUE DATE
